Aquatic Habitat Assessment

Common Methods

Support for this publication
was provided by

Sport Fish Restoration Act Funds

administered by the

**U.S. Fish and Wildlife Service
Division of Federal Aid**

Aquatic Habitat Assessment

Common Methods

Edited by

Mark B. Bain
and
Nathalie J. Stevenson

American Fisheries Society
Bethesda, Maryland

Suggested Citation Formats

Entire Book

Bain, M. B., and N. J. Stevenson, editors. 1999. Aquatic habitat assessment: common methods. American Fisheries Society, Bethesda, Maryland.

Chapter within the Book

Meixler, M. S. 1999. Regional setting. Pages 11–24 *in* M. B. Bain and N. J. Stevenson, editors. Aquatic habitat assessment: common methods. American Fisheries Society, Bethesda, Maryland.

Cover illustration, original drawings, and modifications to figures by Teresa Sawester.

Library of Congress Catalog Number: 99-068788

ISBN: 1-888569-18-2

Printed in the United States of America

American Fisheries Society
5410 Grosvenor Lane, Suite 110
Bethesda, Maryland 20814-2199, USA

Contents

Contributors

Mark B. Bain, U.S. Geological Survey, New York Cooperative Fish and Wildlife Research Unit, Fernow Hall, Cornell University, Ithaca, New York 14853

Eric P. Bergersen, U.S. Geological Survey, Colorado Cooperative Fish and Wildlife Research Unit, Room 201, Wagar Building, Colorado State University, Colorado 80526

Wayne A. Hubert, U.S. Geological Survey, Wyoming Cooperative Fish and Wildlife Research Unit, Box 3166, University Station, Laramie, Wyoming 82071-3166

Kristin K. Arend, Anne S. Gallagher, Thomas C. Hughes, Kristin M. Hynd, Marcia S. Meixler, Katherine E. Mills, Nathalie J. Stevenson, Department of Natural Resources, Fernow Hall, Cornell University, Ithaca, New York 14853

Symbols and Abbreviations

A	ampere		N	newton; normal; north
AC	alternating current		N	sample size
°C	degrees Celsius		NS	not significant
cm	centimeter		n	ploidy; nanno (10^{-9}, as a prefix)
Co.	Company		o	ortho (as a chemical prefix)
Corp.	Corporation		oz	ounce (28.4 g)
cov	covariance		P	probability
DC	direct current; District of Columbia		p	para (as a chemical prefix)
D	dextro configuration		p	pico (10^{-12}, as a prefix)
d	day		Pa	pascal
d	dextrorotary		pH	negative log of hydrogen ion activity
df	degrees of freedom		ppm	parts per million (in the metric system, use mg/L, mg/kg, etc.)
dL	deciliter			
E	east		ppt	parts per thousand
E	expected value		qt	quart (0.946 L)
e	base of natural logarithm		R	multiple correlation or regression coefficient
e.g.,	for example		r	simple correlation or regression coefficient
eq	equivalent		rad	radian
et al.	(et alii) and others		S	siemens (for electrical conductance); south (for geography)
etc.	et cetera			
F	filial generation; Farad		s	second
°F	degrees Fahrenheit		SD	standard deviation
ft	foot (30.5 cm)		SE	standard error
g	gram		sr	steradian
gal	gallon (3.79 L)		tris	tris(hydroxymethyl)-aminomethane (a buffer)
h	hour		UK	United Kingdom
ha	hectare (2.47 acres)		U.S.	United States (adjective)
Hz	hertz		USA	United States of America (noun)
in	inch (2.54 cm)		V	volt
Inc.	incorporated		V, Var	variance (population)
i.e.,	that is		var	variance (sample)
IU	international unit		W	watt (for power); west (for geography)
k	kilo (10^3, as a prefix)		Wb	weber
kg	kilogram		yd	yard (0.914 m, 91.4 cm)
km	kilometer		α	probability of type I error (false rejection of null hypothesis)
l	levorotary			
L	levo configuration		β	probability of type II error (false acceptance of null hypothesis)
L	liter (0.264 gal, 1.06 qt)			
lb	pound (0.454 kg, 454g)		Ω	ohm
log	logarithm (specify base)		μ	micro (10^{-6}, as a prefix)
M	mega (10^6, as a prefix); molar (as a suffix or by itself)		′	minute (angular)
m	meter (as a suffix or by itself); milli (10^{-3}, as a prefix)		″	second (angular)
mi	mile (1.61 km)		°	degree (temperature as a prefix, angular as a suffix)
min	minute		%	per cent (per hundred)
mol	mole		‰	per mille (per thousand)

Introduction

1

Mark B. Bain

1.1 Purpose of This Manual

Habitat is now the basis of most impact assessments and resource inventories, and it is the basis of many species management plans, mitigation planning, and environmental regulation. Habitats are relatively stable through time, easily defined in intuitive physical terms, and provide a tangible resource for negotiations and decision making. Numerous and varied methods of analyzing and reporting habitat conditions have been developed by federal, state, provincial, and private agencies, and habitat assessment approaches vary greatly among regions of the continent. The great variability in methods and an unusually wide range of practices have impeded the ability of agencies to share and synthesize information. A diversity of methods is desirable in the initial stages of a rapidly developing field, but enough time has passed to assess the state-of-knowledge and identify the best of the currently used methods and techniques.

This manual is intended to provide fisheries biologists with a limited set of techniques for obtaining aquatic habitat data. The manual also describes the range of information collected and used in agency habitat analyses. Agencies planning habitat programs should review the synthesis of established and documented methods being used in North America (Appendix 1) and the planning recommendations in Chapter 2. Then, the remaining chapters should be reviewed to determine what types of habitat data should be included in the agency's program.

1.2 Development of This Manual

A brief history of *Common Methods* will explain how this manual developed. In 1995, the American Fisheries Society (AFS) and the

U.S. Fish and Wildlife Service organized a joint project in response to the need for more uniform habitat assessment methods. These organizations wanted to evaluate the wide array of habitat assessment methods being used by agencies with inland fisheries management responsibilities, and to select a set of standard techniques. Enhancing the comparability among diverse agency methods was the primary goal.

The joint habitat project has produced several products culminating in this manual. In 1997, a symposium titled "Aquatic Habitat Analysis Methods: An AFS Initiative and Some Recent Advances" was organized by Steve Filipek and Mark Bain for the 127th Annual Meeting of the American Fisheries Society in Monterey, California. Some presentations from that symposium have since been published in *Fisheries*. Wayne Hubert and Eric Bergersen provided basic guidance for developing aquatic habitat assessment programs. Their recommendations were published (Hubert and Bergersen 1998) in *Fisheries* and appear in this manual as Chapter 2. Mark Bain, Tom Hughes, and Kristin Arend reported the results of a North American survey of fisheries agencies and the methods used for aquatic habitat assessment. This work was published (Bain et al. 1999) in *Fisheries* and it is included in Appendix 1 of this manual. One major product, Armantrout's (1998) *Glossary of Aquatic Habitat Inventory Terminology*, was compiled to develop consistent terminology for habitat assessment work. These preliminary products provided the foundation for a manual of common methods for inland aquatic habitat assessment.

The survey of North American fisheries agencies reported in Appendix 1 and Bain et al. (1999) was especially important. This study surveyed state, provincial, federal, and private organizations to obtain documentation of methods being used to assess aquatic habitats in the inland waters of North America. The methods documents were used to characterize the attributes of current practices. Most state, provincial, and federal agencies with fisheries management responsibility have been using some type of established (i.e., well documented and in use) method for aquatic habitat assessment. However, a substantial number (~30%) of the agencies have been relying on ad hoc procedures. The survey showed that the dominant purpose for having an established method was to standardize measurements and data collection techniques.

Most of the 52 methods reviewed by Bain et al. (1999) target habitats associated with flowing waters, but many of the methods are used exclusively with lakes and reservoirs. Methods for stream habitats included a wide array of measurements emphasizing channel structure, water movement, substrate, cover, and riparian habitat. The lentic habitat methods emphasized the littoral zone, shallow-water physical structure, and riparian areas. Many of the methods had long lists of habitat attributes that could be measured, and many measurements appeared redundant even within single assessment methods. The methods review identified 705 different habitat variables although a large portion of these were similar. Habitat attributes such as fish cover were being measured in such varied ways that any meaningful synthesis was not possible across regions, provinces, states, and even through time within single agencies.

After the methods review and synthesis were completed, the focus of the AFS project shifted to seeking a large reduction in the diverse forms of habitat data being collected by fisheries agencies and organizations. Our selection of methods and techniques provides a range of habitat assessment practices that vary in effort, precision, and detail. Nevertheless, widespread use of the techniques described in this manual will greatly reduce the variability in approaches and types of data being used in habitat assessment programs.

1.3   Selection of Methods and Techniques

This manual is organized into 16 method chapters that each contain a choice of related techniques. Methods are collections of techniques that have a common purpose. We considered an agency habitat assessment method to be all techniques described in a program manual or instruction document. For this manual, we selected techniques for a particular class of habitat data (e.g., substrate, lake morphology, water temperature) and grouped them into a method chapter covering the habitat attribute. The content of the 16 method chapters was chosen by synthesizing the list of 705 habitat data inputs that came from the comprehensive review of agency methods (Appendix 1). The list was organized by grouping the inputs into themes, and these themes became the topics of the 16 chapters. Each chapter was then planned by (1) reviewing the techniques that were documented and being used by fisheries agencies; (2) considering related techniques from any available source; and (3) selecting the fewest techniques that provide a range of choice in effort, intensity and sophistication. In addition to these considerations, selection of a technique recognized the time required to obtain measurements and data, the need for specialized equipment and training, and other factors related to the cost of the assessment and the feasibility of widespread use. Some of the techniques described here are combinations and modifications of current practices or new techniques assembled in such a way to approximate the effort, gear, and level of sophistication reflected in current methods. In general, the selection process emphasized commonly used techniques rather than the latest advancements in research literature. Hence, we titled this manual *Common Methods*.

Some may feel that recommending common methods will tend to stifle investigation, innovation, and progress. It was clear from our interactions with fisheries agencies that their habitat assessment methods are advancing at a rapid pace, and most agencies are using their first, well-developed and documented assessment method. Researchers are also producing new technologies and techniques regularly. Therefore, we recommend that AFS strive to review, improve, and update the set of methods contained in this manual, and that subsequent editions track this rapidly advancing field. New and innovative techniques should be included in *Common Methods* as they gain broad acceptance by practitioners. For now, however, we believe the methods and techniques presented here represent the good practices in current use and are generally applicable to routine agency habitat assessment needs. The use of methods that are reliable, documented, and applied in reasonably uniform ways will advance the aims of the U.S. Fish and Wildlife Service and American Fisheries Society effort to foster comparability among agency methods.

Assessment site selection was a key issue that divided methods into distinct and contrasting groups in the survey of agency methods. We found that specific but inconsistent approaches were being used to design assessment programs. Almost all current agency methods determine assessment site location and size using one of the following approaches: principles of geomorphology (e.g., multiples of stream width), field investigator judgment (ad hoc), and past experiences (fixed site sizes). Also, assessment sites were located on the basis of representativeness, random selection, or investigator judgment. The survey found there were some efforts to expand the scope of habitat assessment by using multiple sites for watershed or for regional assessment of habitat resources. We did not attempt to address this complex issue in this manual because of the sharply contrasting approaches used among the agencies. This key aspect of habitat assessment warrants focused investigation to provide managers with guidance on tradeoffs associated with the different decisions.

Successful design of habitat assessment programs also rests on selecting methods and techniques with a full understanding of the choices available and the advantages and limitations of each. Read and understand the entire method presentation so appropriate techniques can be chosen and adapted to agency needs, region of interest, and water types. Fisheries biologists interested in selecting techniques for a specific type of habitat data should review the appropriate chapters and consider the recommended techniques. This manual does not specify what techniques should be used in aquatic habitat analyses; rather, we believe the method information, planning guidance, and technique descriptions will lead to a much more consistent set of habitat data than is now being assembled in North America. This would advance the state-of-the-art of aquatic habitat analysis, and it would promote comparability among agency programs and information.

1.4 Acknowledgments

This manual was prepared as part of an American Fisheries Society project funded by the U.S. Fish and Wildlife Service. Robert Kendall, Robert Rand, Eric Wurzbacher, and Beth Staehle of AFS assisted in many ways and improved our work throughout the effort. Beth Staehle provided final editorial expertise and Teresa Sawester did most of the graphics and illustrations. The AFS Fisheries Management Section led the project, and members of the Section assisted in the work leading up to this manual, particularly Steve Filipek, Robert Wiley, Wayne Hubert, Eric Bergersen, and Neil Armantrout. Finally, a long list of reviewers commented on the first version of all chapters, their reviews truly exceeded normal expectations for length and value; they helped greatly in improving this manual.

Approaches to Habitat Analysis

2

Wayne A. Hubert and Eric P. Bergersen

Habitats for fishes are the places where individuals, populations, or assemblages can find the physical and chemical features needed for life. Habitat features include water quality, spawning sites, feeding areas, and migration routes. Habitat quality affects fish abundance and size as well as the species composition. Problems with inadequate, improper, or excessive fish habitat information gathered by fisheries workers are widespread and can be attributed to poorly defined goals for collecting information.

We define successful fish habitat management as a planned sequence of activities that creates or augments various habitats needed to maintain or enhance the abundance of specified species. The key word is *planned*. Planning is the selection and prearrangement of events for the attainment of an objective. In many cases, the excitement of data gathering and the sense of expedience can prompt people to get busy with something familiar and tangible but with little chance of achieving specified goals. Thus, these professionals are lured into a seductive activity trap. The success of habitat management does not start with choosing methods but with applying the fisheries management process (Krueger and Decker 1993). The process involves (1) setting goals, (2) defining objectives, (3) identifying problems, (4) implementing actions to address problems, and (5) evaluating actions to determine if objectives have been achieved. Before any habitat analysis is conducted, a clear purpose and justification for collecting data must be agreed on.

Many protocols exist for habitat analysis, which vary in purpose and types of data gathered. By deciding goals, managers can evaluate individual approaches to habitat analysis. We propose four primary goals for applying habitat analysis.

1. **Inventorying** (i.e., reconnaissance, baseline information, or documentation of resource condition). Current habitat condi-

---

This chapter previously appeared in Fisheries 23(5): 20–21.

tions are described throughout a broad spatial scale, and the data are stored in a retrievable manner.

2. **Analyzing habitat quality.** Managers identify habitat features that impede fish abundance or production.
3. **Monitoring effects of land use.** Possible changes to and degradation of fish habitat associated with land use practices in a watershed are monitored. Changes may result from human activities such as logging or road construction.
4. **Assessing habitat improvement activities** (i.e., evaluating the success of management). When management defines specific, quantifiable objectives for a habitat improvement project or program, changes in habitat are evaluated through a systematic assessment program.

Within the defined purposes of habitat analysis, an array of sampling principles must be considered (Platts et al. 1987; Willis and Murphy 1996). Standardized sampling protocols are required to describe temporal trends (McMahon et al. 1996). Techniques must be repeatable and be sufficiently accurate and precise to detect changes. Terms and units of measure, sampling methods, criteria for evaluation, spatial and temporal scales, stratification and classification systems, and data storage and analysis should all be standardized. However, the specific dimensions of habitat analysis differ depending on the goal of the project.

2.1   Inventorying

One goal of habitat analysis might be describing baseline conditions. Here, the manager is concerned with broad reconnaissance and development of an information base for an extensive area. The basinwide inventory technique developed by the U.S. Forest Service is an example of a standardized inventory system developed and applied by an agency (Hankin and Reeves 1988). Interpreting data from inventories is frequently difficult because sampling techniques often are imprecise; the data give little insight into the habitat features that may affect fish; and the spatial and temporal dimensions of the data often are incongruent or not easily depicted. Vast amounts of inventory data are gathered and stored with little understanding as to how they may be used by resource managers, especially by fisheries managers. Many inventories are simply (and unfortunately) the end product of the activity trap.

2.2   Analyzing Habitat Quality

Analyzing habitat features that limit fish production is a challenge to fisheries managers. Such analyses include observation and interpretation of the habitat features that are affecting fish survival. Hunter (1991) stated that when a manager finds an attribute that does not meet a fish's minimum requirements, a limiting factor is identified. *Limiting factors* can be viewed as anything that impedes the dynamics of an organism or population. They also can be defined as the critical minimum requirements for survival. Fisheries managers want to identify limiting factors and relieve them to enhance fish production and achieve the production potential, ecological capability, or optimum productivity of a system.

However, few habitat analysis tools focus on identifying limiting factors or the relations between habitat and production potential. Such analytical approaches need to go beyond identifying the life stage or habitat feature that may limit production, and instead reveal the root cause of the problem. Sampling through the year or throughout a watershed may be necessary. As fisheries managers, we have barely begun to develop analytical tools that can identify limiting factors and specific habitat improvement needs. Much of the sampling and many of the analyses provide data that do not or cannot identify limiting factors. When this happens, the effort becomes little more than a form of occupational therapy, the activity trap.

2.3 Monitoring Effects of Land Use

Land managers also may analyze habitat to evaluate the effects of land use patterns on habitat, justify the implementation of management programs, or substantiate an organization's position in court. Platts et al. (1987) described a six-step process to identify effects of land use: (1) specify information that must be collected for use in the planning and resource management process, (2) determine a tentative approach for collecting information, (3) conduct pilot sampling to obtain preliminary data to determine the accuracy and precision of sampling, (4) collect information, (5) analyze information and interpret results, and (6) process the information for use in the management process.

Also within this process are the needs to (1) establish decision criteria at the time sampling protocols are designed, (2) identify habitat variables that respond to land use activities and provide insight into fish habitat quality, and (3) define the level of statistical confidence required of the sampling data. To conduct the analysis within reasonable costs, fisheries professionals stratify (zones, reaches, habitat types, or seasons) sampling to minimize variation and reduce measurement error. Hawkins et al. (1993) provide one example of a widely accepted stratification procedure for stream habitat. When developing a sampling protocol, managers must consider aquatic systems as continuums with interactions that occur throughout a watershed.

Monitoring programs to analyze the effects of land use on fish habitat that have defined goals and objectives, follow the general process of Platts et al. (1987), and have rigorous sampling protocols, decision criteria, and analytical protocols are rare. Unfortunately, many efforts to monitor the effects of land use on fish habitat also fall into the activity trap.

2.4 Assessing Habitat Improvement Activities

Managers assess habitat improvement activities to gain insight into the effects of management activities on fish habitat quality and fish populations. A goal is to assess whether management objectives have been met. Assessing habitat management activities involves three levels (Kershner et al. 1991).

1. Implementation: Were the prescribed improvement activities correctly implemented?
2. Effectiveness: Were the objectives achieved?
3. Validation: Were the objectives met because of the planned habitat changes?

Such an assessment requires measuring habitat features prior to any action, habitat improvement activities to determine whether they meet specification, and the same habitat features following management action for an extended time. Platts et al. (1987) proposed a process for assessing habitat management efforts that is more site-specific, focuses on improving habitat conditions to achieve management objectives, and involves prescribed activities. It also demands a more rigorous sampling design, including clearly defined hypotheses, control areas that do not receive management treatments, and efforts to control confounding factors that may harm or influence conclusions. Due to the time required to allow responses to management activities, assessing habitat improvement activities takes a long time. Consequently, management agencies must conduct long-term assessments to allow responses to occur, assure that accuracy and precision of standardized sampling techniques are maintained, and recognize the continuing obligation to monitor past management activities. Most efforts to assess habitat improvement activities lack some of the dimensions required to effectively assess long-term success of activities. Because of a focus on producing tangible habitat improvements, the assessment process is often incomplete. As a result, both the habitat improvement activities and the assessment efforts may do little more than hamper our quest to understand what is actually going on when we modify aquatic habitats—the activity trap again.

Regional Setting

3

Marcia S. Meixler

3.1 Introduction

3.1.1 Background

Broad patterns of climate and geology influence many properties of aquatic habitats such as hydrology, nutrient and temperature regimes, groundwater potential, dominant substrates, stream morphology, and the formation of various types of wetlands and lakes. Aquatic habitat is largely a product of the surrounding land and climate (Likens and Bormann 1974; Hynes 1975; Omernik and Griffith 1991); identifying the regional setting makes it easier to group similar habitats and recognize local variability (Warren 1979; Whittier et al. 1988). Resource management agencies often strive to use habitat assessments for broad, holistic, and ecosystem scale analyses (Omernik and Bailey 1997; Bailey 1998) and methods have been developed to classify habitat information in large spatial frameworks. Spatial frameworks are classification systems where a region is recognized as having a similar mosaic of aquatic habitats that contrast with those of the adjacent or different regions (Bailey et al. 1978; Hughes et al. 1986; Omernik 1987; Lyons 1989; Omernik and Bailey 1997). Several spatial frameworks are in use by fisheries management agencies for assessment and inventory of aquatic resources, and four of these are detailed below: ecoregions, watersheds, hydrologic units, and physiographic provinces.

Ecosystem or regional management must consider multiple spatial scales since aquatic systems occur in a hierarchy of varying sizes (Bailey 1998). Further, the factors that constrain or influence aquatic systems operate at different space and time scales. Some agencies have adopted hierarchical classification systems (Figure 3.1) where a series of levels are organized so that finer classified regions nest

Domains

Divisions

Provinces

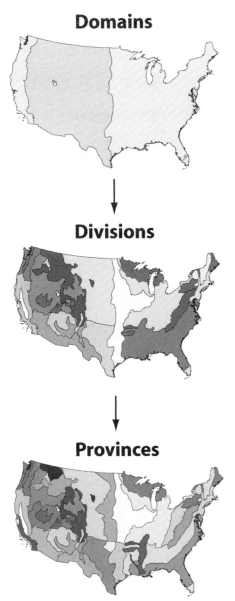

Figure 3.1   Example of a hierarchical structure in spatial frameworks (Bailey 1995).

within the next larger class, and all classes in a level are mutually exclusive of the others in that level (Bailey et al. 1978; Bailey 1995). In this way, precise, locally sensitive regions can be used while still maintaining a useful classification for larger regions (Lyons 1989). Ecosystem level stratification can increase monitoring efficiency, improve data interpretation and trend detection, and provide a framework for assessing and reporting on water quality (Omernik and Griffith 1991).

Ecoregions, the first of four spatial frameworks presented, were developed as broad, hierarchical, landscape classifications. Ecoregion classifications provide an overview of the spatial patterns and the most influential environmental variables for aquatic habitats. Ecoregion classifications are based on a few easily measured or well-known characteristics (e.g., climate, geology, landform) which shape the contained aquatic habitats and could account for much of the variation in the distribution of biotic communities (Bailey 1983; Bailey and Hogg 1986; Omernik 1987). Ecoregions provide managers, planners, and scientists with a common base for communicating a habitat's regional setting. Habitat issues addressed in the context of ecoregions are typically ranges in chemical quality, biotic assemblages, lake trophic state, and management of lands. Finally, ecoregions can be used in selecting reference or monitoring sites, and extrapolating habitat assessment results regionally (Bailey 1983; Rohm et al. 1987).

Watersheds, the second type of spatial framework, are defined as topographic areas within which apparent runoff drains to a specific point on a stream or to a water body such as a lake (Omernik and Bailey 1997). The term basin is often used to describe large watersheds such as those for major rivers. Watersheds are the most common spatial units used by fisheries management agencies in habitat assessment activities and in framing guidelines for controls and remediation (Omernik and Griffith 1991). Watersheds accumulate the surface and subsurface flow of water up gradient from a habitat assessment site. Consequently it is possible to document factors that could influence habitat quality, such as upstream pollution sources and nonpoint source runoff (Omernik and Bailey 1997).

A third spatial framework is the U.S. Geological Survey's (Seaber et al. 1994) hydrologic units that are composed of watersheds, segments of watersheds, and sometimes adjacent areas in between watersheds (Omernik and Griffith 1991). Hydrologic unit maps and codes provide a standardized base for locating, coding, retrieving, indexing, and inventorying hydrologic data and are useful in many water resource management activities (Omernik and Griffith 1991).

The fourth and final spatial framework is physiographic provinces or broad regional units with similar landform characteristics. These provinces are defined primarily from topography in combination with tectonics, geologic structure, lithology, and erosion and sedimentation processes (Hanson 1998). Physiographic provinces and drainage basins have often been used for many years to explain fish distributions (Miller 1958; Pflieger 1971; Trautman 1981; Hughes et al. 1987; Whittier et al. 1988).

3.1.2 Selection of Techniques

The four classification techniques were selected to provide choices in usage, applicability, and practicality. All could be used collectively to obtain a full description of the regional setting for habitat assessments. Table 3.1 compares and contrasts the key characteristics of the four classification systems.

Ecoregion classification synthesizes information on terrestrial variables, which can lead to insight into the broad habitat characteristics of water bodies. Neither watersheds nor physiographic provinces provide similar information (Hughes et al. 1987). This holistic approach to regional classification reveals relationships better than single-factor classifications (Bailey et al. 1978). However, ecoregion classification is not effective with limited geographic areas and individual waters (Lyons 1989).

Watershed frameworks are appropriate for fisheries management agencies to use when assessing the relative contribution of human activities to habitat quality by stream or water body. How-

Table 3.1   Comparison of the ecoregion, watershed, hydrologic unit, and physiographic province spatial frameworks.

Spatial framework	Attributes	Delineation	Primary uses	Geographical coverage
Ecoregions	Multifactor Geographical Regional Hierarchical	Climate, soils, geology, hydrology, landform, elevation	Studies of the health, integrity, and quality of environmental resources over large areas	Global, continental, national, regional, and state
Watersheds	Single factor Geographical Regional Hierarchical	Topographic divides	Studies of the effects of natural and anthropogenic phenomena on water quality and quantity; used mostly at the local level	National, regional, state, and local
Hydrologic units	Single factor Geographical Regional Hierarchical	Surface topography; not true watersheds	Geographical cataloging; coordination, storage, and retrieval of survey information; manipulation, organization, and dissemination of data on a geographic, political, and hydrologic basis	National and state
Physiographic provinces	Single factor Geographical Regional Hierarchical	Topography, structure, and, to a lesser extent, climate	Identification of fish distributions	Global, continental, national, regional, state, and local

ever, the larger river basin scale does not account for changes in local habitat characteristics due to surrounding land uses (Whittier et al. 1988). Another drawback of watershed classification is that information in a watershed cannot be extrapolated. Geoclimatic and biological characteristics as well as anthropogenic disturbances in larger regions seldom correspond to watersheds or basins (Omernik and Bailey 1997).

Hydrologic units are defined by single-factor delineation of boundaries much like watersheds, but most hydrologic units are not true topographic watersheds (Omernik and Bailey 1997). The units are useful for capturing and managing hydrologic data and are used in water resource management (Omernik and Griffith 1991). The drainage divides used to delineate hydrologic units help to explain spatial differences in fish assemblages and abundance (Omernik and Bailey 1997). However, hydrologic units do not correspond to patterns in vegetation, soils, land forms, land use, and other characteristics that control or reflect spatial variations in surface waters. The true spatial variations in quality are masked (Omernik and Griffith 1991) when hydrologic units are used as a primary framework to aggregate data, illustrate patterns, and suggest management options.

Physiographic provinces are hierarchical and based on a single-factor for delineation of boundaries. Physiographic provinces are traditionally used by ichthyologists to describe fish distributions in aquatic systems (Pflieger 1971; Trautman 1981); however, Hughes et al. (1987) found that physiographic provinces and river basins were less useful than Omernik's ecoregions for explaining historical fish distribution patterns in Oregon. Although physiographic provinces can account for many of the attributes that shape aquatic systems, they do not necessarily correspond with soil, climate, land use, and other attributes (Omernik 1987). Despite this, physiographic provinces are considered more accurate classifications than traditional river basins for defining regional settings (Omernik and Bailey 1997), and they have a long history of use for resource assessment (e.g., Powell 1896).

3.2 Ecoregion Identification

3.2.1 Rationale

Ecoregions are relatively uniform areas defined by generally coinciding boundaries of several key geographic variables. Delineation of regions is accomplished by examining patterns in the homogeneity of several terrestrial variables expected to have major influences on aquatic ecosystems (Hughes et al. 1986). Ecoregions have been defined holistically using a set of physical and biotic factors (e.g., geology, landform, soil, vegetation, climate, wildlife, water, and human factors) rather than a single factor (Commission for Environmental Cooperation 1997). This delineation lends itself to a hierarchical scale, from very site-specific aquatic conditions to large broad scale ecosystems, where finer classified regions nest within the next larger classification category.

The first national scale ecoregions emerged in the mid-1980s with Wiken's (1986) classification for Canada and Omernik's (1987) for the United States. The Commission for Environmental Cooperation (1997) organized ecoregional classifications of Canada, the United States, and Mexico to provide a common framework for the ecoregional classification of North America, and recently several classification systems have emerged on a global scale (Busch and Sly 1992; Angermeier and Schlosser 1995; Bailey 1995; Jensen et al., in press). Ecoregions are used to

1. compare the regional similarities and differences in hydrology, temperature and nutrient regimes;
2. identify the natural characteristics and potential of aquatic systems;
3. determine precise regional criteria to measure and evaluate aquatic ecosystem integrity;
4. establish water quality standards which reflect regional patterns of tolerance, resilience to and recovery from human impacts;
5. set management goals for nonpoint source pollution;
6. locate monitoring, demonstration, or reference sites;
7. extrapolate regional information from existing site-specific studies (Rohm et al. 1987);
8. predict the effects of changes in land use and pollution controls (Omernik 1987);
9. estimate ecosystem productivity and likely responses to management action (Hughes et al. 1986);
10. evaluate temporal and spatial changes in ecological integrity (Bailey 1983); and
11. plan at the national and international levels (Bailey 1978).

Two of the most commonly used ecoregional systems, Bailey's and Omernik's, are described for use in this section. Bailey's objective in creating an ecoregion map was to provide a broad synthesis of our current knowledge about the ecosystem geography of the United States and a useful reference for persons who desire a comparative overview (Bailey 1978). Macroclimate, the climate that lies just beyond the local modifying irregularities of landform and vegetation, is interpreted as having an overriding effect on the composition and productivity of ecosystems from region to region (Bailey 1998). Information on macroclimate and prevailing plant formations was used to classify the continent into three levels of detail. Bailey's coarsest hierarchical classifications include 4 (for the United States) domains, 15 divisions, 53 provinces, and 194 sections. These regional classes are based largely on broad ecological climate zones (identified by Koppen [1931] and modified by Trewartha [1968]) and thermal and moisture limits for plant growth (Bailey 1995, 1998). Domains are groups of related climates, and divisions are types of climate based on seasonality of precipitation or degree of dryness or cold. Divisions are further subdivided into provinces based on macrofeatures of the vegetation. Provinces are distinct enough to describe the zonation in altitude of mountains and the climatic regime of the adjacent lowlands. Provinces include characterizations of land-surface form, climate, vegetation, soils, and fauna (Bailey 1995). The subdivision of provinces into sections is based on physiography (i.e., landform and geology) which exerts control over habitats within climatic–vegetation zones (Bailey et al. 1994). Sections include characterizations of geomorphology, stratigraphy and lithology, soil taxa (temperature, moisture regimes), potential natural vegetation, elevation, precipitation, temperature, growing season, surface water characteristics, and disturbance (Bailey et al. 1994). Some areas of the country are mapped further to subsections with detailed subsection descriptions. Information from domains, divisions, and provinces is used for modeling, sampling, strategic planning, and assessment. Information from sections and subsections is used for strategic, multi-forest, statewide, and multi-agency analysis and assessment. Information from smaller regions, called landscapes, is used for forest planning; watershed analysis and even smaller land unit classifications are intended for planning and analysis of projects and management areas.

Omernik's ecoregion system was formed in response to a need for an alternative classification for regionalizing water resource management (Omernik 1987) and to distinguish regional patterns of water quality in ecosystems as a result of land use. Omernik's system is suited for classifying aquatic ecoregions and monitoring water quality because of the ecological way it was developed; its level of resolution; its use of physical, chemical, and biological mapped information; and a lack of necessary data collection (Hughes et al. 1986). Omernik's system has been extensively tested and found to correspond well to spatial patterns of water chemistry and fish distribution (Whittier et al. 1988). Much like Bailey's system, Omernik's system is hierarchical, dividing an area into finer regions in a series of levels. There are 9 level I ecoregions in North America, 32 level II classes, and 78 level III classes (September 1996 version; U.S. Environmental Protection Agency 1996). The description of level III ecoregions includes characterizations of land surface form, potential natural vegetation, land use, and soils. Portions of the United States have been further subdivided into level IV ecoregions.

Omernik delineated regional boundaries by analyzing the most important component maps and sketching out regions that appeared to be homogeneous in their land use, land surface form, soils, and potential natural vegetation (Omernik 1987). Some regions could be easily delineated by the distinctiveness of all four characteristics. Less distinct regions were identified by broader groupings of some of the characteristics or by using fewer characteristics. The boundaries were then ascertained from the initial sketches and with characteristic tables which typified each component region. Overlay combinations were examined and final delineations shaped for each ecoregion (U.S. Geological Survey 1997). Once completed, the map of the United States was divided into ecoregions, and an attribute was added to indicate if the polygons were either most typical or generally typical of a particular region. Consequently, two map versions are available: one version of the map represents the ecoregions, and the other version of the map delineates the most typical portions of each ecoregion. The most typical portions are defined as areas sharing all of the characteristics of the ecoregion, whereas the generally typical portions of each ecoregion share most, but not all, of the same characteristics.

3.2.2 Preparation

▶ Develop familiarity with web browsing if using the Internet to locate site. Develop competence with ARC/INFO geographic information systems if downloading the digital map version. Assemble map or description of sites to locate, and acquire necessary maps and ecoregion descriptions as described below.

▶ Bailey's ecoregion map and descriptions can be obtained from one of the sources below.
  - Paper maps and accompanying literature (1995 version): available from U.S. Forest Service, Fort Collins, Colorado, 303-498-1768; fine-scale maps can be obtained from the U.S. Forest Service Regional Office in each state.
  - CD-ROM: contact the Southern Geometronics Service Center for information on a CD-ROM for some western U.S. regions.
  - ARC/INFO geographic information systems files: free digital compressed ARC/INFO ecoregion maps are available at http://www.fs.fed.us/institute/ecolink.html
  - Digital versions in ARC/INFO format can also be obtained from the U.S. Forest Service, Ecosystem Management Analysis Center, on a cost-of-production basis.
  - Ecoregion descriptions are available for domains, divisions, provinces, and sections at http://www.fs.fed.us/institute/ecolink.html

▶ Omernik's ecoregion map and descriptions can be obtained from one of the sources below.
  - Paper version: Omernik, J. M. 1987. Ecoregions of the conterminous United States. *Annals of the Association of American Geographers* 77:118–125. Level I–III ecoregion maps and some finer scale level IV maps with detailed ecoregion descriptions can be ordered from the U.S. Environmental Protection Agency Environmental Research Laboratory, Corvallis, Oregon, 541-754-4450.
  - ARC/INFO geographic information systems files: Omernik's level III ecoregions (1987 version) in digital version are available as one of the datasets on the CD-ROM, Conterminous U.S. AVHRR Companion Disc from Customer Services, U.S. Geological Survey, EROS Data Center, Sioux Falls, South Dakota 57198, 605-594-6151 (fax: 605-594-6589; email: custserv@edcserver1.cr.usgs.gov).

- ARC/INFO Internet files: digital level III ecoregion maps of the conterminous United States are available at http://www.epa.gov/OST/BASINS/gisdata.html (download BASINS core data) with documentation at http://www.epa.gov/envirofw/html/nsdi/nsditxt/useco.txt

3.2.3 Procedure

- **Identify ecoregion.** Determine the location of the study site on the ecoregion map and note Bailey's hierarchical classifications: domains, divisions, provinces, and if possible the sections and subsections. Also note Omernik's level I, level II, level III, and if possible, the level IV ecoregions. One or both ecoregion systems could be used. County, state, or U.S. maps may be helpful.

- **Describe ecoregion.** Use the ecoregion descriptions (either or both systems) to characterize the regional setting of the assessment site (example in Box 3.1 with Bailey's ecoregion description, and Box 3.2 with Omernik's ecoregion description). If the study site appears to be on an ecoregion line, use the descriptions of the ecoregions on either side of the line and determine which best fits the study site area. Often a stream or river assessment site is influenced more by the upstream ecoregion which produces most of the water, wood, and sediments than by the ecoregion in which the site is located. Note the provinces or sections drained by the watershed of the site if interested in longitudinal stream effects.

3.2.4 Notes

Omernik's classification system has been extensively tested and is widely used by state water quality agencies, many of whom are collaborating with Omernik to produce level IV ecoregions. Due to the extensive testing proving the utility and accuracy of Omernik's classification system, Whittier et al. (1988) concluded that Omernik's ecoregions represented the most appropriate framework for classification of lotic systems.

3.3 Watershed Identification

3.3.1 Rationale

Watersheds are delineated along the topographic divide (see Chapter 4, Drainage Basins) or more simply by noting which streams belong to the same drainage network. Watershed identity is used primarily at the local level to classify effects of natural and anthropogenic phenomena on water quality and quantity. Watersheds are also the appropriate units for explaining fish distribution (Miller 1958) due to the interconnectedness of river basins (Whittier et al. 1988).

Box 3.1   Example of regional setting form with Bailey's ecoregion system.

Investigator: __Jane Howard__   Date: __01 August 1998__

Study site name: __Allegheny River__   Code #: __USEPA Reach 05010001 15 6.30__

Watershed name: __Allegheny River watershed__

Reference: __Smith, C. L. 1985. The inland fishes of New York state. The NYS Department of Environmental__

__Conservation, Albany, NY__

Hydrologic unit name and code: __Upper Allegheny 50010001__

Reference: __USEPA Surf Your Watershed http://www.epa.gov/surf2/hucs/05010001/__

Physiographic province: __Appalachian plateau__

Reference: __Hanson, L. Physiographic provinces of the United States. http://www.salem.mass.edu/~lhanson/__

__gls210/phpr_index.htm__

Ecoregion name and number: __Laurentian mixed forest — Province 212__

Reference: __Bailey, R.G. 1995. Description of the ecoregions of the United States. 2nd ed. Pub. No. 1391__

__Washington, D.C.__

Site description:

About the ecoregion

Land-surface form: Most of this province has low relief, but rolling hills occur in many places. Lakes, poorly drained depressions, morainic hills, drumlins, eskers, outwash plains, and other glacial features are typical of the area, which was entirely covered by glaciers during parts of the Pleistocene. Elevations range from sea level to 2,400 ft (730 m).

Climate: Winters are moderately long and somewhat severe, but more than 120 days have temperatures above 50°F (10°C). Average annual temperatures range 35–50°F (2–10°C). A short growing season imposes severe restrictions on agriculture; the frost-free season lasts 100–140 days. Snow usually stays on the ground all winter. During winter, the province lies north of the main cyclonic belt; but during summer it lies within this belt, and the weather is changeable. Average annual precipitation is moderate, 24–45 in (610–1,150 mm); maximum precipitation comes in summer.

Vegetation: This province lies between the boreal forest and the broadleaf deciduous forest zones and is therefore transitional. Part of it consists of mixed stands of a few coniferous species (mainly pine) and a few deciduous species (mainly yellow birch, sugar maple, and American beech); the rest is a macromosaic of pure deciduous forest in favorable habitats with good soils and pure coniferous forest in less favorable habitats with poor soils. Mixed stands have several species of conifer, mainly northern white pine in the Great Lakes region, with a mixture of eastern hemlock. Eastern red cedar is found in the southeast. Pine trees are often the pioneer woody species that flourish in burned-over areas or on abandoned arable land. Because they grow more rapidly than deciduous species where soils are poor, they quickly form a forest canopy; but where deciduous undergrowth is dense, they have trouble regenerating and remain successful only where fire recurs. Fires started by lightning are common in this province, particularly where soils are sandy and there is a layer of dry litter in summer.

Soils: The greatly varying soils include peat, muck, marl, clay, sand, gravel, and boulders, in various combinations. Spodosols are dominant in New England and along the Great Lakes coast; Inceptisols are dominant farther inland. The Alfisols are medium to high in bases and have gray to brown surface horizons and subsurface horizons of clay accumulation.

Fauna: In winter, the shorttail weasel (ermine) and snowshoe hare turn white, as they do in polar provinces. The black bear, striped skunk, marmot, chipmunk, and two genera of jumping mice all pass the winter in hibernation. So do badger and the striped ground squirrel that live in the western parts of the province. Beaver and muskrat remain active all winter, working beneath the ice that covers the lakes and streams. Ptarmigan also turn white in winter. Many other birds, especially insectivorous species, migrate south. Common summer resident birds include the white-throated sparrow, northern junco, and the yellow-bellied sapsucker.

Comments: __Bailey's province 212 is within division 210 and domain 200__

Box 3.2   Example of regional setting form with Omernik's ecoregion system.

Investigator: <u>Jane Howard</u>   Date: <u>01 August 1998</u>

Study site name: <u>Allegheny River</u>   Code #: <u>USEPA Reach 05010001 15 6.30</u>

Watershed name: <u>Allegheny River watershed</u>

Reference: <u>Smith, C. L. 1985. The inland fishes of New York state. The NYS Department of Environmental Conservation, Albany, NY</u>

Hydrologic unit name and code: <u>Upper Allegheny 50010001</u>

Reference: <u>USEPA Surf Your Watershed http://www.epa.gov/surf2/hucs/05010001/</u>

Physiographic province: <u>Appalachian plateau</u>

Reference: <u>Hanson, L. Physiographic provinces of the United States. http://www.salem.mass.edu/~lhanson/gls210/phpr_index.htm</u>

Ecoregion name and number: <u>Northern Appalachian Plateau and Uplands — 60</u>

Reference: <u>Omernik, J.M. 1987. Aquatic ecoregions of the conterminous United States. Annals of the Association of American Geographers 77(1):118-125</u>

Site description:

About the ecoregion

Land-surface form: open high hills, tablelands with moderate to considerable relief

Potential natural vegetation: northern hardwoods (maple, birch, beech, hemlock)

Land use: mosaic of cropland, pasture, woodland, and forest

Soils: inceptisols

About the physiographic province

Geomorphology: Moderately to heavily dissected plateau with surface elevations ranging from 1,000 to 4,500 feet (305 to 1372 m). The plateau surface is tilted to the east and is separated from the Valley and Ridge province by a prominent escarpment formed by parallel retreat. Sandstones (e.g., Pocono ss.) create a resistant cap rock.

Geology: Composed of gently dipping sedimentary rocks ranging in age from Devonian through Permian. Foreland basin deposits shed eastward from the rising orogenic belts. The Catskill Mountains are comprised of the Acadian clastic wedge. Deposition of the Ordovician Queenston clastic wedge followed the Taconic orogeny. Portions of the plateaus region that is heavily dissected are referred to as "mountains," less dissected areas are "plateaus." The mountains are residual hills formed by extensive dissection of the plateau. The Plateau in New York, and parts of Pennsylvania and Ohio were glaciated.

Resources: Coal (bituminous), oil and gas, limestone, salt

Comments:

Watersheds have been widely used by resource management agencies to organize reports on the status of water quality in individual states, evaluate the effectiveness of stream buffer strips, clarify nonpoint source–stream nutrient level relationships, and map sensitivity of surface waters to acidification. Omernik and Bailey (1997) compared ecoregion and watershed frameworks and concluded that basins and watersheds are appropriate units for resource management agencies to assess the relative contribution of human activities to the quality and quantity of water at specific points.

3.3.2 Preparation

▶ Assemble description of sites to locate, necessary maps, watershed identities commonly used in regional or local management, and descriptive information of regional watersheds. Local, provincial, or state maps may be useful for locating study sites near cultural landmarks (e.g., roads, towns).

3.3.3 Procedures

■ **Identify watershed.** Select the watershed and optionally the larger river basin from maps showing streams and rivers that include the sites of habitat analysis. Notes can be entered on a regional setting form like the example in Box 3.1 and Box 3.2.

3.3.4 Notes

The U.S. Environmental Protection Agency Surf Your Watershed web site (http://www.epa.gov/surf/) can be used to determine the scale of watershed and river basin identities. The web site provides information by watershed so it serves as an example of management scale designations in many parts of the United States.

3.4 Hydrologic Units

3.4.1 Rationale

Hydrologic unit maps, created by the U.S. Geological Survey, provide information on the drainage, hydrography, culture, political, and hydrologic boundaries of the river basins of the United States including Alaska, Hawaii, Puerto Rico, and the Caribbean. These maps depict basic hydrological and political areal planning units, and provide a standard geographical framework for water resource and related land resource planning (Seaber et al. 1994). A hierarchical system was used by designating unique names and codes for 21 major geographic regions (based on surface topography), then subdividing these into 222 subregions designated by the U.S. Water Resources Council, then into 352 accounting units of the U.S. Geological Survey's National Water Data Network, and finally into 2,149 cataloging units of the U.S. Geological Survey's Catalog of Information on Water Data (Seaber et al. 1994).

The 21 major geographic regions are composed of the drainage area of a major river or combined drainage areas of a series of rivers. The second level of classification, the 222 subregions, include the area drained into a river system, a reach of a river and its tributaries in that reach, a closed basin, or a group of streams forming a coastal drainage area (Seaber et al. 1994). The third level of classification includes subdivisions of subregions. Cataloging units, the finest level of classification, are geographic areas representing part or all of a surface drainage basin, a combination of drainage basins, or a distinct hydrologic feature. The cataloging units are generally greater than 700 square miles in area (1,813 km^2).

These four levels of subdivisions are collectively referred to as hydrologic units. The boundaries of these hydrologic units were adapted from several publications: Federal Interagency Committee on Water Resources (1961); U.S. Department of Agriculture (1963, 1970); U.S. Water Resources Council (1970); U.S. Geological Survey (1973); and state planning maps. Political subdivisions are also encoded in the map using the Federal Information Processing Standards codes issued by the U.S. National Bureau of Standards (U.S. National Bureau of Standards 1983). Two basic criteria were followed in delineating boundaries: (1) all boundaries were hydrologic within the United States, though regions and subregions end at international boundaries, and (2) all smaller units nest within the next larger unit.

Hydrologic unit maps are used by water resource organizations for geographical cataloging, coordination, storage and retrieval of survey information and manipulation, organization, and dissemination of data on a geographic, political, and hydrologic basis. The units are widely accepted for use in planning and describing water use and land use activities (Seaber et al. 1994). Agencies are using hydrologic units for managing natural resource data (water rights, water resources, field inventories and surveys, electric generating plants), presenting stream survey and monitoring results, storing and retrieving water quality data, and mapping land cover. The mapping of hydrologic units by the U.S. Geological Survey began in 1972 to provide a standardized nationwide hydrologic reference system for use by a broad range of natural resource agencies.

3.4.2 Preparation

▶ Acquire hydrologic unit maps for the region of interest (see http://www.nationalatlas.gov/hucsm.html or contact the state office of the U.S. Geological Survey Water Resources Division) and habitat analysis site maps or descriptions. Detailed information on cataloging units can be found at the U.S. Environmental Protection Agency Surf Your Watershed web site (http://www.epa.gov/surf/).

3.4.3 Procedure

■ **Identify hydrologic unit.** Determine the location of the habitat analysis sites on the hydrologic unit map, and note the names of the major geographic region, subregion, accounting unit, and cataloging unit. Record hydrologic unit information and any notes as shown on the regional setting form (see example in Boxes 3.1 and 3.2).

3.4.4 Notes

Hydrologic units are not true topographic watersheds and they lack direct correspondence to waters with similar quality and quantity characteristics (Omernik and Bailey 1997).

3.5 Physiographic Provinces

3.5.1 Rationale

Physiographic provinces are the simplest subdivisions of a land area into hierarchical natural regions. Delineation of physiographic provinces is based on topography (mountains, plains, plateaus, and uplands; Atwood 1940) and, to a lesser extent, climate which governs the processes that shape the landscape (weathering, erosion, and sedimentation; Hunt 1967). The major physiographic provinces of the United States were described by Powell (1896), adopted by geographers, and later refined (Fenneman 1931, 1938). Since the 1930s, several versions of physiographic provinces have been published at the state and national levels with maps and descriptions of characteristics.

   Recent delineations of the United States have created 11 major divisions (the broadest hierarchical level) and 34 natural regions (subdivisions of major divisions) called physiographic provinces which include descriptions of climate, vegetation, surficial deposits and soils, water supply or resources, mineral resources, and additional information on features particular to a province where applicable (Hunt 1967). For the most part, the boundaries between provinces are sharp, consisting of a distinct change in structure or topography. However, several provinces grade into one another and boundary lines are necessarily arbitrary (Hunt 1967). Physiographic provinces (Pflieger 1971; Trautman 1981) and drainage basins (Miller 1958) have traditionally been used in aquatic research to identify fish distributions (Hughes et al. 1987; Whittier et al. 1988).

3.5.2 Preparation

▶ Assemble descriptions and maps of habitat analysis sites, physiographic province maps, and descriptions of province characteristics. Physiographic maps and province descriptions can be obtained in different forms (maps, reference books, and Internet) and spatial coverages: earth (e.g., Chesser 1975), North America (e.g., Atwood 1940; Lobeck 1948), United States (e.g., Hanson 1998), regional (e.g., Miller 1990; Olcott 1995; U.S. Geological Survey 1999b), and states (e.g., Texas Bureau of Economic Geology 1998; U.S. Geological Survey 1998; Maryland State Archives 1999). Some state ichthyological references, such as Pflieger (1975), carry an introduction to physiographic provinces with maps and province characteristics. Detailed information about physiographic provinces of the United States can be found at http://www.salem.mass.edu/~lhanson/. Digital maps can be found at http://water.usgs.gov/GIS/. Local, provincial, or state maps may be useful for locating study sites near roads and towns.

3.5.3 Procedure

■ **Identify physiographic provinces.** Determine the location of the study site on the map of physiographic provinces and note the description of characteristics. If the study site appears to be on the border line between physiographic provinces, read the descriptions of the provinces on either side of the line and determine which best fits the study site area. A suggested format for data recording is displayed in Boxes 3.1 and 3.2.

3.5.4 Notes

Often a reach is influenced more by the upstream physiographic province which produces most of the water, wood, and sediments than by the province in which the reach is located.

Drainage Basins

4

Anne S. Gallagher

4.1 Introduction

4.1.1 Background

A drainage basin is an area of the earth's surface occupied by a surface stream or lentic water body together with all of the tributary streams, surface, and subsurface water flows. Drainage basins are important to understanding the characteristics of stream habitats (Frissell et al. 1986). The boundaries of a drainage basin are used to explain biogeographic distributions of fish species. Basin features are a factor in predicting flood patterns, estimating sediment yield, and predicting water availability and quality. The downstream transfer of water, sediment, nutrients, and organic material all influence the characteristics of stream habitats. It is therefore important to understand the geologic, hydrologic, morphologic, and vegetational setting of a stream in its basin.

Large-scale features of a drainage basin include the size, shape, and relief of the basin. Small-scale features include measurements of channel length and slope, storage capacity, and drainage density of the stream network within the basin. Each of these geomorphic properties can be used to compare basins. Finally, understanding drainage basin attributes aids habitat investigators when interpreting field data. This chapter has no field component because basin-scale attributes are regularly estimated from maps and digital terrain and land cover data. The information discussed here should be used to complement the biotic and abiotic data acquired through field-work.

4.1.2 Selection of Techniques

Three techniques are reviewed below for characterizing different aspects of a drainage basin. The first technique involves quantifying geomorphic properties of a river basin. These properties include a variety of measurements that are best used to compare the environmental settings of different habitat assessment sites in the same region. Quantifying geomorphic properties requires detailed work with topographic maps or geographic information systems (GIS) data. The second technique, stream ordering, provides an easy method for classifying streams in a drainage network based on their size and type of tributary junctions. Stream order is probably the single most common descriptor of fish sampling sites reported by fisheries biologists, and stream order is routinely reported in fisheries field studies. The third technique is used to classify the land use and land cover of the basin. Land cover and use information is increasingly being made available in digital form.

4.2 Geomorphic Properties

4.2.1 Rationale

The most useful basin attributes for characterizing the setting of a stream and drainage basin are described here. The properties can be measured and estimated by one of two basic approaches. Basic area and length measurements can be done by hand on topographic maps. Alternatively, a computer program of the U.S. Geological Survey (Basinsoft; Harvey and Eash 1996) can be used with GIS data to compute the geomorphic properties.

4.2.2 Preparation

▶ Acquire U.S. Geological Survey (USGS) topographic maps at 1:24,000 scale (preferred, or use 100,000 scale) that cover the entire drainage network of streams and adjacent drainage basin streams.

▶ Gain access to a GIS unit with a digitizer, software, and a trained technician. Alternatively, obtain a polar planimeter or a 100 dot-per-square-inch transparent overlay with a map measurer (see Figure 16.1) and ruler.

4.2.3 Procedures

■ Delineate the drainage basin on a topographic map. The drainage basin divide (border) should approximate all locations at which surface run-off splits flow into and away from the basin. For all of the land enclosed in the drainage divide, precipitation drains by gravity into the stream or water body within the basin. Re-

view the topographic map features outlined in Box 4.1 to properly interpret map notations. Draw the drainage divide according
to the following steps and refer to Figure 4.1 for an example. The
drainage divide should begin and end at the mouth of the stream
or river being studied and should enclose only its tributaries.
Draw the drainage divide perpendicular to each of the contour
lines it crosses. On flat areas, such as along contour lines, divide
in half the areas between streams of different basins. This division should approximate the location at which surface waters
split flow and fall naturally by gravity into their respective basins. If only a portion of a drainage basin is being considered
(e.g., the drainage area of a study site along a stream segment),
the drainage divide line may turn abruptly and proceed straight
down to the channel at the study site.

Estimate the total drainage area by measuring the map area enclosed by the drainage divide in one of three ways.

1. Digitize the drainage basin into a GIS file and obtain the
    drainage area using the computer software. Note that some
    drainage basins may already be digitized by state or federal
    agencies and this information may be accessible to the public.

2. Outline the drainage basin with a polar planimeter (a device
    that calculates the area of any plane) by moving the tracer
    point along the drainage divide and recording the enclosed
    area in vernier units. Convert the vernier units to a conve-

---

Box 4.1   Topographic map features for determining a drainage
divide.

⊕ Streams on a topographic map are represented by blue lines. Solid
   blue lines represent perennial streams. Dashed blue lines represent
   intermittent streams.

⊕ Water bodies are blue.

⊕ Brown lines are contour lines, which mark areas of equal elevation.
   Closely spaced contour lines mark areas of steep gradient, while
   distant contour lines indicate a more gradual slope.

⊕ Contour lines tend to form "V"s where they intersect streams
   and "M"s above stream junctions. These "V"s and "M"s point
   upstream. Use this to help locate all upstream contributing stream
   segments.

⊕ Note the location of the headwater streams (i.e., streams with no
   tributaries). They should be enclosed in the drainage divide separated from the headwater streams supplying different drainage
   basins. Only streams that flow into the study site should be included
   in the drainage divide.

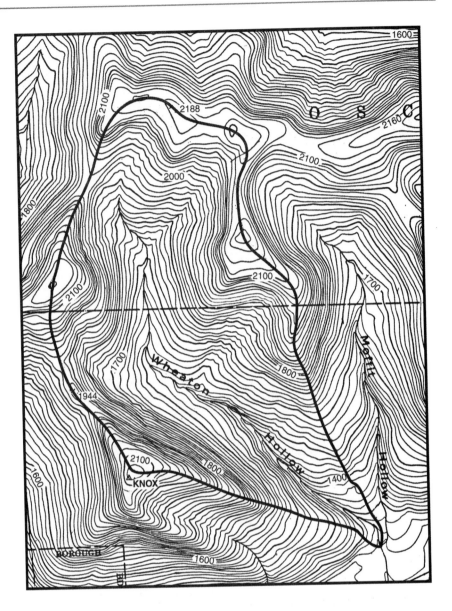

Figure 4.1   Example drainage divide on a topographic map.

nient area measurement (e.g., square kilometers) based on the scale of the map and the conversions provided with the planimeter.

3. Use a 100 dot-per-square-inch transparent overlay placed over the drainage basin. Count the total number of dots falling within the basin divide and one-half of the number of dots falling on the divide line. If the basin is larger than the overlay, divide the basin into smaller sections and measure each smaller area. Check Table 16.1 for the correct conversion factor (note map scale) and multiply the total number of dots counted by this conversion factor to obtain the area of the basin in square kilometers. Note that the precision of this

measurement can be improved by increasing grid density on the overlay.

Once the drainage divide is drawn on a map and the area has been estimated, the geomorphic properties can be estimated, measured, or computed. Each of the geomorphic properties listed below includes a definition and explanation of its importance to basin characterization.

Basin length. Basin length is estimated as the straight-line distance between the mouth of the basin and the drainage divide nearest to the source of the main stream. Use a map measurer or a ruler to measure a line drawn on the map. Basin length is used to calculate drainage shape.

Basin relief. Basin relief is the difference in elevation between the highest and lowest points in the basin. It controls the stream gradient and therefore influences flood patterns and the amount of sediment that can be transported. Hadley and Schumm (1961) showed that sediment load increases exponentially with basin relief.

Basin relief ratio. The basin relief ratio index is the basin relief divided by the basin length. It is useful when comparing basins of different sizes because it standardizes the change in elevation over distance.

Basin surface storage. The percentage of the basin covered in lentic and impounded water bodies, including wetlands (optional), reflects the surface storage capacity of the basin. Determine the basin surface storage by measuring the area of each lake or impounded water body. Wetland areas will have to be estimated because the borders are not delineated on topographic maps. Follow the instructions for measuring area given above. Add all water body and wetland areas and divide this sum by the drainage area.

Drainage density. An index of the length of stream per unit area of basin is calculated by dividing the drainage area by the total stream length. This ratio represents the amount of stream necessary to drain the basin. High drainage density may indicate high water yield and sediment transport, high flood peaks, steep hills, low suitability for agriculture, and high difficulty of access.

Drainage shape. An index of drainage shape is computed as a unitless dimension of drainage area divided by the square of basin length (Horton 1932). It describes the elongation of the basin and is useful for comparing basins. If two basins have the same area, the more elongated one will tend to have smaller flood peaks but longer lasting flood flows (Gregory and Walling 1973).

Main channel slope. Main channel slope is an estimate of the typical rate of elevation change along the main channel that drains the basin. This measurement is often related to peak flow magnitude and flood volume. Estimate the main channel slope by measuring the length of the main channel from the mouth of the stream or the study site to the mapped source of the main stream. At each stream channel bifurcation, follow the fork with either the higher stream order number (explained below) or the longer pathway to a stream source. Mark off 10% and 85% of the main channel length on the map. Estimate the elevation in meters at the 10% and 85% distance points, using the contour lines on the topographic map. Compute the main channel slope as follows:

Slope = (elevation at 85% length − elevation at 10% length) / 0.75 (main channel length).

Total stream length. Total stream length is the sum of the lengths of all perennial streams within a basin as shown on a topographic map. Determine the total stream length by measuring the length of each perennial stream section with a map measurer. Sum these individual stream lengths. The summed stream lengths determine the total amount of stream habitat in a basin and the availability of sediment for transport (Meador 1998).

The Basinsoft computer program of the U.S. Geological Survey produces estimates for all of the above geomorphic properties and several more. The program requires four digital map layers: drainage basin boundary, hydrography, hypsography, and a lattice elevation model. Habitat investigators with access to GIS usually find that the computer program is the most efficient method for basin geomorphic assessment. The software is described by Harvey and Eash (1996), and the U.S. Geological Survey is continuing development of this software. For the most recent information, contact: Craig Harvey, U.S. Geological Survey, Water Resources Division, 308 South Airport Road, Pearl, Mississippi 39208-6649, 601-933-2983 (email: caharvey@ usgs.gov).

4.3 Stream Order

4.3.1 Rationale

Stream order, or classifying streams based on the number and type of tributary junctions, is an easily obtained, useful, but general indicator of stream size, discharge, and drainage area. There are several techniques for determining stream order. Horton (1945) developed a system for ordering streams that Strahler (1964) later refined. In this system, the headwaters of a stream are designated first order, and the confluence of two streams of order n forms a stream of order $n + 1$. For example, the confluence of two second-order streams forms a third-order stream, but the confluence of a second- and third-order stream yields a third-order stream. Given this system, relationships can be developed between stream order and the number of stream segments within the drainage network, and between stream order and stream length. The higher the stream order, the fewer the number of streams at that order and the longer the stream length. In addition, the amount of water drained by a stream increases with stream order. As stream order increases from order n to order $n + 1$, there are usually three to four times fewer streams, each of which is generally twice as long and drains four to five times as much area (Allan 1995).

Shreve (1967) developed the link system of ordering streams in which the orders of upstream tributaries are summed. For example, the confluence of a second-order and a third-order stream forms a fifth-order stream. This system relates a given stream segment to upstream and downstream influences within its basin. This information may be useful when analyzing fisheries data. For example, a small tributary stream that feeds a large river might have a large link number, which would indicate that although the stream is small, it may have large river species (Meador 1998).

Both of the techniques are outlined below. Choosing which technique to use for ordering streams should depend on how the information will be used. The Strahler system of stream ordering is used most frequently, and unless otherwise noted, it is assumed that this is the technique used.

4.3.2 Preparation

▷ Acquire USGS topographic maps at 1:24,000 scale that cover the entire drainage network of streams. All stream ordering methods depend on the source and scale of maps used to count tributaries. By common practice, it is assumed that stream ordering is done at the 1:24,000 scale. Other scales may be used, but always use the same source and scale of map when ordering streams and making comparisons among basins. Be sure to report the scale when a scale other than 1:24,000 is used.

4.3.3 Procedures

▪ For both the Strahler and the link systems, a first-order stream is the furthest upstream section of a stream (headwater stream), and a stream section is a length of stream between any two intersections (sources, mouths, or tributary mouths). Leopold et al. (1964) recommended counting both perennial and intermittent streams when using a 7.5-min USGS topographic map. Others count only perennial streams. Either approach may be used if it is used consistently.

- For the Strahler system, order streams as follows. Two first-order streams meet to form a second-order stream. Two second-order streams meet to form a third-order stream. This pattern continues such that when two streams of order n meet, they form a stream of order $n + 1$. When one stream is met by another stream of a lesser order, its order does not change. Both streams must be of the same order when they flow together to create a stream of the next higher order. See Figure 4.2A for an example.

- For the link system, order streams as follows. Add the stream order numbers of the upstream tributaries to get the order of the resulting stream. Two first-order streams meet to form a second-order stream, and two second-order streams meet to form a fourth-order stream. See Figure 4.2B for an example.

4.4 Basin Land Cover

4.4.1 Rationale

Land cover comprises the geology, soils, vegetation, and land use of an area. Geology influences the shape of drainage basin patterns, streambed material, water chemistry, and base streamflow. Soils influence infiltration rates and vegetation types, and vegetation has a large role in determining channel bank stability, surface runoff, and water loss through evapotranspiration (Dunne and Leopold 1978). Land use can effect soil permeability, vegetation, and most parts of the hydrologic cycle. Characterizing these interrelated components of a drainage basin provides important information for interpreting field and biological data.

4.4.2 Preparation

▷ Obtain printed or digital maps of land cover for the drainage basin being studied. Thematic digital maps of land use, geology, soils, and vegetation are available from the USGS EROS Data Center (http://edcwww.cr.usgs.gov) and the USGS Global Land Information System (http://edcwww.cr.usgs.gov/webglis/glisbin/glismain.pl). Local or regional maps and aerial photographs may provide better resolution and more recent data than national maps.

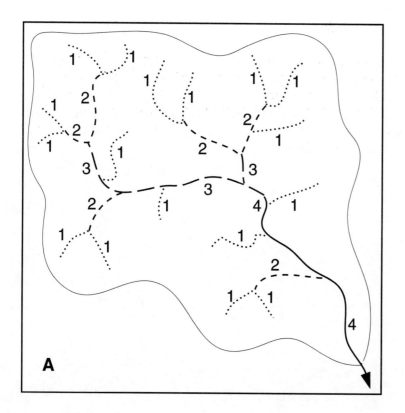

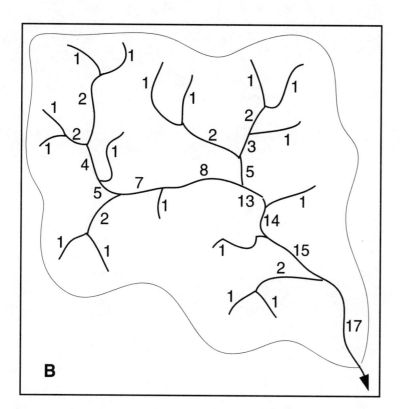

Figure 4.2   Numbering stream orders using the Strahler system (A) and the link system (B).

4.4.3 Procedures

■ Geographic information systems with thematic maps and the drainage area divide can be used to break down land cover features in area measures (km^2) or percentages. The same values can be obtained by manually working (area estimates described above) with map overlays produced from the thematic maps or similar information.

Water Body Identification 5

Marcia S. Meixler

5.1 Introduction

5.1.1 Background

The term water body refers to any source of water or hydrologic feature such as a stream, river, lake, pond, canal, wetland, reservoir, or spring (see definitions in Table 5.1). Thorough and detailed identification of water bodies for sampled sites is important for organization in databases, identification by other data users, and relocation on maps or in the field. In addition, carefully documented databases with precise location identifiers can be used to create spatial hydrological representations using geographic information systems (GIS). Once in GIS, current data can easily be related to previously collected data and examined for changes over time or used in land and resource management planning over large geographical areas.

Three distinct forms of documentation are described in this chapter: position identification, location coding, and descriptive attributes. Each form of documentation is important on its own merit for particular data uses; however, when all used together, a water body is thoroughly identified and documented. Position identifiers such as latitude, longitude, elevation, and universal transverse mercator (UTM) coordinates are helpful in locating the water body on topographic maps. Location coding assigns a unique number to each water body. This is the primary requirement for relational data, because it links field data to point, line, and polygon entities which represent water bodies in GIS. Descriptive attributes such as water body name and type, land ownership, accessibility, and general comments are important field identifiers for the site.

Table 5.1   Water body types and definitions from Armantrout (1996) with designation codes for use on field forms and in databases.

Type	Code	Description
Catchment, pit	C	Basin for catching water from surface runoff or seepage. Pond formed by accumulation of water in an area excavated to catch and store water.
Bog, marsh, wetland	B	Lands where saturation with water is the dominant factor determining the nature of soil development and the types of plant and animal communities living in the soil and on its surface. Soils or substrates that are at least periodically saturated with or covered by water, and differ from adjoining non-inundated areas.
Spring, seep	S	An issue of water from the earth taking the form, on the surface, of a stream or body of water. A small spring, pool, or other place where a minor amount of groundwater has emerged to the land surface or into a stream. A seep describes an amount of water coming to the surface which is too small to be considered a spring.
Well	W	A hole dug or drilled into the earth, or a natural spring source of water.
Guzzler	G	Water entrapment and containment structure used primarily to provide water for wildlife and livestock in arid regions.
Pond	P	Body of standing water smaller than a lake.
Gully, wash	Y	A depression or channel with water seasonally or periodically and formed by water such as the dry bed of an ephemeral stream.
River	R	Natural stream flowing in a definite course or channel, or a series of diverging and converging channels. Includes streams, creeks, brooks, runs.
	R1	Any river or stream not specified by other codes below.
	R2	Falls: a reach that is either a waterfall, drop spillway, or a reach of rapids.
	R3	Headwater: a headwater reach that has no reaches above it but one or several reaches on its downstream end.
	R4	Terminal: a reach downstream from which there is no other reach (e.g., a reach that terminates into an ocean or the ground).
Lake	L	Body of fresh or saline water of considerable size completely surrounded by land.
	L1	Any lake not specified by other codes below.
	L2	Reservoirs: a body of impounded water stored for the purpose of altering the timing of flow for future use such as irrigation, flow augmentation, treatment, and power generation.
	L3	Cirque lake: a small body of water occupying a cirque (a deep, steep-walled recess in a mountain caused by glacial erosion) depression dammed by a rock lip, small moraine, or both.

Table 5.1   Continued.

Type	Code	Description
	L4	Moraine lake: a lake formed by glacial drift blocking a valley or drainage courses.
	L5	Potholes, kettles: a lake in a drift depression made by the wasting away of a detached mass of glacier ice that had been either wholly or partly buried in the drift.
	L6	Oxbow lake: a lake formed in an abandoned riverbed which has become separated from the main stream by a change in the course of the river.
	L7	Pasternoster lake: a chain of smaller lakes in a glaciated valley formed by the corrosive action of ice.
	L8	Thaw lake: a lake or pond basin in permafrost areas that are formed by the thawing of ground ice. A pool of water on the surface of sea ice or formed by accumulation of melt water on large glaciers.
	L9	Beaver pond: impoundment made by beavers.
	L10	Playa: broad, shallow sheets of water that quickly gather and almost as quickly evaporate, leaving mud flats to mark their sites.
	L11	Alkali: a lake formed in low depressions. Water evaporation deposits fine sediments and dissolved minerals which form a hard surface if mechanical sediments prevail or a crumbly powdered surface if efflorescent salts are abundant.
	L12	Coastal: a lake on any plain that has its margin on the shore of a large body of water, particularly the sea, and generally represents a strip of recently emerged sea bottom.
	L13	Gravel pit: lake formed in excavations resulting from the removal of sand and gravel.
	L14	Rift: a lake formed in depressions resulting from the intersection of a fault plane with the land surface.
	L15	Sink: a lake formed in a depression or poorly drained area formed where the underlying rock dissolves and water collects.

5.1.2 Selection of Techniques

Water body identification techniques can either work together to achieve detailed site documentation or each can be used independently to record select information for future reference. Location information is easy to obtain in the office or at the study site and is useful for identifying the position of the site on topographic maps or in GIS. Most global positioning system units used in the field give fairly accurate latitude, longitude, elevation, and UTM data, reducing the need to obtain this information from topographic maps.

An assessment site or water body identifying code should be made up entirely of numbers, unique for every water body, objectively determined (e.g., each user would determine the same code independently), available at a fine scale, and used nationally. The closest system for this is the nationally used U.S. Environmental Protection Agency (USEPA) reach coding system, which assigns a unique 17-digit number for each water body (U.S. Environmental Protection Agency 1994). This coding system is oriented toward relating database information on streams to spatial hydrology in GIS and, therefore, the coding information is provided to the public in digital format compatible with GIS. Individuals without access to GIS may have difficulty obtaining paper maps that show the USEPA reach code numbers. Another drawback of this system is the scale. Only water bodies visible at the 1:100,000 scale will be represented in the USEPA reach system. There is currently no national coding system for water bodies at a scale finer than 1:100,000. General coding information, the U.S. Geological Survey (USGS) hydrologic accounting unit and catalog unit codes, can be used to give an approximate location of the water body. These codes are easily identifiable, made up entirely of numbers, unique, objective, and used nationally.

Finally, descriptive attributes (water body name and type, land ownership, and accessibility) are easy to determine and useful in finding field sites on future visits. Descriptive attributes take time to complete, but there are no other disadvantages to using this technique.

5.2 Position Identification

5.2.1 Rationale

Often data are shared by many biologists or agencies to enhance databases or create applications in GIS. Consequently, it is important for data users to be able to easily locate sampled water bodies on topographic maps. Latitude, longitude, elevation, and UTM coordinates can be quickly and easily obtained from USGS topographic maps in the office or the field.

Latitude, longitude, and UTM coordinates define the location of a point on earth in two-dimensional space. The addition of elevation to latitude and longitude coordinates enables the description of a point in three-dimensional space. The combination of latitude, longitude, and elevation is the most common coordinate system in use today. Locations in GIS applications are often defined by UTM coordinates and are as easy to read as latitude, longitude, and elevation values. Dana (1998) provides a thorough review of these coordinate systems.

Lines of longitude run north and south and lines of latitude run east and west. The longitudinal line at zero degrees is called the prime meridian and the latitudinal line at zero degrees is the equator. Values for longitude and latitude are given in degrees, minutes, and seconds with an indication of position north (N) or south (S) of the equator for lines of latitude and east (E) or west (W) of the prime meridian for lines of longitude. When defining a point, use both latitude and longitude values and note whether the value is north, south, east, or west. Elevations are defined in feet or meters of altitude above sea level. A typical format for defining position using longitude, latitude, and elevation is shown on the water body identification form in Box 5.1.

The universal transverse mercator projection was designed by the U.S. military and uses a system of rectangular zones defining an area in 6° longitudinal strips extending from 80° south latitude to 84° north latitude. Each zone has a central meridian situated 3° in longitude from each border; therefore, in zone 17, the central meridian is at 81° west longitude since the zone extends from 78 to 84° west longitude (see Dana 1998 for a graphical depiction). North and south coordinates called northings, east and west coordinates called eastings, and a zone number are used to describe geographic location using UTM coordinates. Eastings are measured as distance in meters from the central meridian and northings are measured as distance in meters from the equator. An additional 500 km are added to the easting coordinate value to ensure positive coordinates (called a false easting) and 10,000 km are added to values for positions south of the equator (called a false northing). Box 5.1 shows the typical format for defining position using UTM coordinates.

5.2.2 Preparation

▶ Acquire USGS topographic maps at 1:24,000 scale (or use 100,000 scale) from 1-800-USA-MAPS (1-800-872-6277), or 1-800-HELP-MAP (1-800-435-7627), or from a local store. If unsure which maps you will need, see the U.S. Geological Survey (1999a) Geographic Names Information System at http://mapping.usgs.gov/www/gnis/gnisform.html

▶ Prepare data recording sheets.

5.2.3 Procedures

■ **Record basic information.** Locate the water body on the appropriate map and record basic topographic information on a data sheet for each water body or habitat. Note the USGS topographic map name provided on the map in the bottom right corner. Also record the county, state, date of map, and scale (bottom, center of map).

■ **Identify latitude and longitude coordinates.** Determine and record the latitude and longitude of the water body from the topographic map; include degrees, minutes, seconds, then direction (N or S for latitude, E or W for longitude). To determine the latitude for water bodies that do not fall directly on latitude and longitude lines, (1) align a straightedge horizontally from the water body to the point of intersection with the edge of the map,

Box 5.1   Example of water body identification form use.

Observer(s): Jane Howard _____   Date: ___01 August 1998_____

Position identification

USGS topographic map name __Knapp Creek_____   Scale _1:24,000_____

County __Cattaraugus_____   State _New York_____   Date of map _1979_____

Latitude _42'05"24°N_____   N or S   Longitude _78'30"6.6°W_____   E or W

Elevation _1410 Feet_____   Feet or meters

UTM __4662572mN_____   706928.6mE_____   Zone _17_____

Water body coding

General coding:

    USGS hydrologic accounting unit: name _Ohio Region, Allegheny River Basin_____   code# _050100_____

    USGS catalog unit: name _Upper Allegheny_____   code# _05010001____

USEPA reach code __05010001 15 6.30_____

State or other codes: code name: _WIN_____   code#: _PA-53_____

State or other codes: code name: _NY state code_____   code#: _21NYDECA___

Descriptive attributes

Water body name __Allegheny River_____

Water body type __R1_____   Land ownership _Private 4_____

Accessibility and location __Site along right side of Rt. 60 heading west after bridge leaving the town

    of Allegany; mostly chest deep water, but canoe helpful in places_____

Photographs: Roll _2_____   Frames _5,6,7_____

Comments: __Frame explanation: 5 (upstream) , 6 (downstream), 7 (bank erosion); Mucky bottom

_____

_____

_____

_____

(2) find the tick marks for the nearest coordinates and determine their distance from the straightedge using a ruler or instrument with tick marks, and (3) add to or subtract from the nearest coordinate value as necessary to determine the latitude of the water body. For example, on a 1:24,000 scale topographic quadrangle, longitudinal and latitudinal tick marks are 2 min and 30 s apart. If a straightedge intersects the edge of the map four-fifths of the distance above the nearest lower (southern) coordinate value, 30 s should be subtracted from the value above (northern) to determine the latitude of the water body. The process should be repeated using the straightedge in the vertical direction to calculate the longitude of the water body.

- **Estimate elevation.** Determine the elevation of the water body from the contour lines on the topographic map. Make sure to note if the value is in feet or meters. The topographic map will have information on the contour interval and units in the bottom, center of the map. Record the elevation interval for the location or use interpolation to obtain a more precise elevation value.

- **Identify UTM coordinates.** Determine the UTM coordinates and zone of the water body from the topographic map. Alternatively, to convert latitude and longitude coordinates to UTM coordinates, look on the Internet: http://www.geod.nrcan.gc.ca/products/html-public/GSDapps/English/online_applications.html (Natural Resources Canada 1999).

5.2.4 Notes

A suggested format for data recording is given in Box 5.1, and a blank data sheet is in Box 5.2.

Latitude, longitude, elevation, and UTM coordinates can also be determined from a precision instrument called a global positioning system (GPS). Specially coded signals from four satellites are processed in a GPS receiver, which then computes position, velocity, and time. Latitude and longitude are usually provided in the geodetic datum on which GPS is based (WGS-84), however, receivers can often be set to convert to other user-required datums (such as UTM, Dana 1998). Global positioning systems are available in many sizes and with varying degrees of sophistication. Several have the ability to store information which can be downloaded directly to a computer. Accuracy of the data from GPS receivers depends on level of noise, bias such as Selective Availability (SA) interference by the U.S. government to maintain optimum effectiveness of the military system, and user error. The noise and bias errors combine to cause typical ranging errors of around 15 m for each satellite signal used by the GPS unit to compute a position (minimum of four satellites). User errors alone (e.g., incorrect GPS unit configuration), can result in errors of hundreds of meters (Dana 1998).

Box 5.2   Water body identification form.

Observer(s): _____   Date: _____

Position identification

USGS topographic map name _____   Scale _____

County _____   State _____   Date of map _____

Latitude _____   N or S   Longitude _____   E or W

Elevation _____   Feet or meters

UTM _____   _____   Zone _____

Water body coding

General coding:

    USGS hydrologic accounting unit: name _____   code# _____

    USGS catalog unit: name _____   code# _____

USEPA reach code _____

State or other codes: code name: _____   code#: _____

State or other codes: code name: _____   code#: _____

Descriptive attributes

Water body name _____

Water body type _____   Land ownership _____

Accessibility and location _____

_____

Photographs: Roll _____   Frames _____

Comments: _____

_____

_____

_____

_____

_____

5.3 Water Body Coding

5.3.1 Rationale

Water body codes are unique, identifying numbers for each stream and lake in the United States. Coded survey data are stored in relational databases for later evaluation, manipulation, and location identification. At present there is no nationwide coding system at a scale finer than 1:100,000. The coding systems presented here include coarse-scale watershed codes and the USEPA reach codes. The coarse-scale codes are from the USGS hydrologic accounting units (sample, Figure 5.1). This information can be used to give a researcher the approximate location of the water body. Finer-scale codes are from the USEPA reach file version 3 (U.S. Environmental Protection Agency 1994). Code numbers are obtained from digital GIS files (example in Figure 5.2) given to the public by the USEPA. The USEPA reach file is only applicable for water bodies that appear on maps at the 1:100,000 scale, but the file has unique 17-digit numbers for each water body segment. The USEPA reach codes are available on a national scale and they are easy to determine. However, this system may be difficult to use if habitats and water bodies appear only on fine-scale maps, and when access to GIS is not readily available. Many states have developed coding systems for water bodies at a fine scale, and these should be used when possible.

5.3.2 Preparation

▶ Acquire USGS topographic maps at 1:24,000 scale (see section 5.2.2), locate water body, and prepare data sheets.

▶ Determine hydrologic unit codes from USEPA's Surf Your Watershed site (http://www.epa.gov/surf/), or obtain a listing of hydrologic accounting units and catalog unit names from USGS Water Supply Paper 2294 (Seaber et al. 1987), available from available from http://water.usgs.gov/GIS/huc.html or the U.S. Geological Survey Information Services, Denver

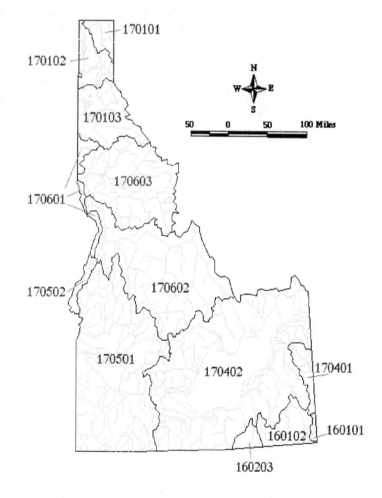

Figure 5.1   U.S. Geological Survey hydrologic units for the state of Idaho. Source: University of Montana(1999).

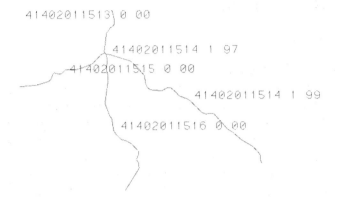

Figure 5.2   Sample stream network map from the U.S. Environmental Protection Agency reach file showing codes for all stream segments.

Federal Center, Box 25286, Denver, Colorado 80225, 1-800-435-7627.

▶   Obtain digital hydrography from the USEPA (1-800-424-9067) or http://www.epa.gov/OST/BASINS/gisdata.html (download Reach File Version 3 data). You must know the hydrologic accounting unit and catalog unit codes when calling (see section 5.3.3). Print a copy of the USEPA reach file (version 3) map with associated reach codes if coding in the field.

5.3.3 Procedures

■   **Coarse-scale codes.** Determine the USGS hydrologic accounting and catalog unit names and codes for the water body from the Internet or the USGS Water Supply Paper 2294.

■   **Fine-scale codes.** Use a topographic map to locate the water body on the digital or paper version of the USEPA reach map (produced by GIS). Determine the reach code (called an "Rf3rchid" code in the USEPA reach program).

5.3.4 Notes

A suggested format for data recording is displayed in Box 5.1, and a blank data sheet is in Box 5.2.

Many states have developed their own systems for identifying water bodies. It maybe useful to locate a paper or digital explanation of the coding system used by your state.

A coordinated effort is underway to combine the features of the USEPA river reach files (RF3) with the USGS digital line graph (DLG-3) hydrography files to create a National Hydrography Dataset (NHD). The goal is a comprehensive digital nationwide 1:24,000-scale dataset, available on the Internet. Each water body at the 1:24,000 scale will be assigned a unique 14-digit code number. The final datasets will be made publicly available. You can track progress of this effort at http://www.usgs.gov or http://www.epa.gov or by searching for "national hydrography dataset" on USGS and EPA web sites.

5.4 Descriptive Attributes

5.4.1 Rationale

Describing surveyed water bodies and habitats is a valuable part of the site identification process. Water body name and type, land ownership, accessibility, and general notes are recorded while at habitat assessment sites. Markings on topographic maps and pictures are helpful if the site has not been previously documented. A water body name can reflect local terminology, and the water body type designation facilitates comparisons among comparable waters (Armantrout 1996). Land ownership identifies the property rights associated with the land surrounding the water body. Accessibility is a short, written description of how to reach the water body. General comments account for anything not covered above.

5.4.2 Preparation

▶ Assemble topographic maps, camera, and data sheet.

▶ Obtain permission to survey on private land, if necessary

▶ Become familiar with the water body if notes are to be completed independently of the habitat assessment.

5.4.3 Procedure

■ Determine the water body name from the topographic map or local knowledge of the area. Using water body type definitions in Table 5.1, determine the type and enter the code on the data sheet. Note any new management actions and the responsible agency. Note site ownership and characterize accessibility as: (1) entry prohibited, (2) access through public property, (3) access not available at all times to all people, (4) public is permitted. Accessibility descriptions should be written descriptively, noting landmarks and road names if applicable. Take photographs of the site and record the roll and frame numbers. Mark the location of the habitats and water body on a topographic map. Additional description of the water body can be included in the comments section of the sample data sheet (Box 5.2).

Stream Reach Surveys and Measurements

6

Kristin K. Arend and Mark B. Bain

6.1 Introduction

6.1.1 Background

Channel dimensions are closely related to the hydrology, local geology, climate, and condition of the watershed. An assessment of channel dimensions provides the finest level of resolution at which a stream reach can be related to the whole stream as well as the entire watershed. Data from channel assessments are typically compiled to develop a detailed description of habitat unit (e.g., pool, riffle, etc.) dimensions, channel form and pattern, discharge, substrate, bank condition, and riparian vegetation. Also, when values are known for certain dimensions, estimates and values of other stream reach characteristics can be calculated. For example, water velocity is directly related to stream width, depth, slope, and channel roughness, and from these values the discharge of a stream can be calculated. Finally, measurements of channel dimensions are frequently used to map assessment sites and scale maps provide accurate descriptions of habitat units.

Cross-sectional and longitudinal (upstream–downstream) profile surveys are conducted along a series of transects spaced throughout a stream reach to create a geomorphic depiction of the assessment site. At each transect, surveyors take measurements and collect data necessary to accurately record the dimensions of a stream site and to precisely quantify the position of stream features. Cross-sectional and longitudinal profile surveys are often conducted along permanent transects so they can be reevaluated over time and during different seasons. Changes in stream hydrology and morphology can then be monitored and related to management or restoration efforts, anthropogenic activities, or natural events.

The objective of a stream reach survey is to deduce a representation of the stream as accurately as possible, without actually sampling it in entirety. Therefore, select survey sites (i.e., stream reaches) that are representative of a stream. Field sketches and dimensional data are used to produce an accurate, representative picture of the stream and to locate the reach for subsequent surveys. General surveys can be conducted throughout the year and under various flow conditions; however, many of the techniques used in reach surveys (e.g., water surface elevation measurements) can only be conducted in wadeable streams during periods of low flow because of equipment limitations and safety concerns. Reach surveys should be conducted at typical low flow conditions when habitat features are most evident.

6.1.2 Selection of Techniques

This chapter presents techniques for conducting two-dimensional map and one-dimensional cross-sectional and longitudinal profile surveys and for measuring channel and habitat dimensions. Many other stream assessment techniques can be incorporated into the reach survey (e.g., reach type classification, channel geomorphic unit identification, riparian vegetation characterization, and fish cover). The following techniques are commonly used, time efficient, and reasonably accurate. They focus on establishing an assessment site, conducting cross-section measurements, developing a scale map, and producing a longitudinal profile. Select specific techniques according to study objectives and equipment and time restrictions. Instructions for using surveying equipment are not provided, but can be found in many survey manuals including some that focus on stream habitats (Gordon et al. 1992; Harrelson et al. 1994).

6.2 Preparation

▶ Field staff should be experienced in the use of surveying equipment and terminology. Practice and the study of survey technique manuals (e.g., Harrelson et al. 1994) are the best ways to gain experience.

▶ Acquire measuring tapes, stakes and flagging, a survey level, a telescoping surveyor's rod, a folding tripod, chest and hip waders, a compass, and material for making field sketches. Two-way radios equipped with headsets are optional but very helpful for communication between surveyors in high gradient streams with rapids.

6.3 Procedures

■ **Select site and transect arrangement.** Choose a section of a stream where channel form and characteristics are representative of the larger stream being assessed. This stream section will be the assessment site. The recommended length of a stream site varies among specialists from lengths equal to 5 to 7 times the average stream width (from channel sequence interval described in Leopold et al. 1964), to as much as 40 times the average stream width (Simonson et al. 1994; Kaufmann and Robison 1995). The time and effort to complete reach measurements increases with site length, so use program objectives and constraints to identify an appropriate stream length. When the site length is determined, locate an assessment site that has common channel features; encompasses one or more riffle and pool sequences; is accessible to field staff; where the upstream and downstream ends line up with habitat breaks (e.g., the head of a riffle or pool); that avoids tributary junctions; and where altered sections are not included unless modified channels are typical for the section or the features of interest. After the site is located, mark the location of transects (cross sections that include the banks up onto the floodplain) with stakes on each bank and flagging. Again, recommendations vary regarding the number of transects to include for a site. Also, uniform channels can be represented with fewer transects than more physically complex channels. As an approximate number, transects can be established every one-tenth of the site length and at the ends (11 total).

■ **Collect transect measurements.** Establish a permanent (for repeated site surveys) or temporary benchmark (see Notes below for benchmarks) near one end of each transect. Use wooden stakes or trees to hold a metal measuring tape or beaded steel wire tag line tight on the transect. Use a level to check that the tape or line is not slanted. Referring to Figure 6.1 (letters in text below correspond to letters in figure), make a series of measurements—in any order—and record them on a sketch of the cross-section, always recording the transect distance. Record (A) the vertical distance between the benchmark and the transect line or tape to establish the actual elevation of all other measurements. Make two measurements that correspond with the thalweg (transect location with the greatest water depth, B): the distance from the tape or line to the stream bottom, and the distance to the water surface. Subtract these measurements to get the maximum water depth. Record the distances from the transect to the stream edges (C). Identify the bankfull water edge (D, see Notes below) on each bank, and record the vertical distance from the transect line to the ground (average the two values if different) and the transect distances. These measurements provide the bankfull width (difference of transect distances) and the bankfull depth (total vertical distance at B minus values at D points).

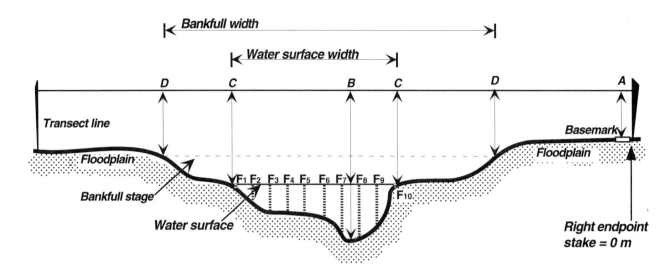

Figure 6.1   Diagram of transect measurements of a stream cross section. Letters are explained in the text.

Record 10 evenly spaced water depths (F_1, F_2, . . . F_{10}) and the corresponding transect line distances. Measure water depth with a level rod, ruled rod, or tape measure. Read the depth on the downstream side of the measuring tool to avoid inaccuracies created by the wave formed by an object in moving water. The depth values can be averaged to get the mean water depth for the cross section. Finally, lay a chain from water edge to water edge (C points) allowing it to follow the bottom contours. Mark the water edge endpoints on the chain and measure the straight distance to get the wetted perimeter to the cross section (subtract islands).

■ **Map the site.** In the field, obtain information for a scale map of an assessment site using a survey level and rod, compass, and tape measures. The basic approach is to survey distances and angles off north from a survey level position to at least one transect endpoint for a set of site transects. Then, the angle off north and distances along the transect can be used to position the transect, water edges, and thalweg in space. Accuracy is much better if both transect endpoints are surveyed. A site sketch is done and measurements are recorded on the sketch with some basic habitat information added as in Figure 6.2. Accuracy will vary depending on the precise combination of tools, steps, and measurements but with care and some survey experience, a reasonably accurate scale map can be assembled within a few hours. Figure 6.2 shows one choice of measurements for a site with five transects. In this example, a survey level is located so both endpoints of each of five transects can be seen. The angles off north and distances (in feet for example) from the survey level to each transect endpoint are recorded and entered on a

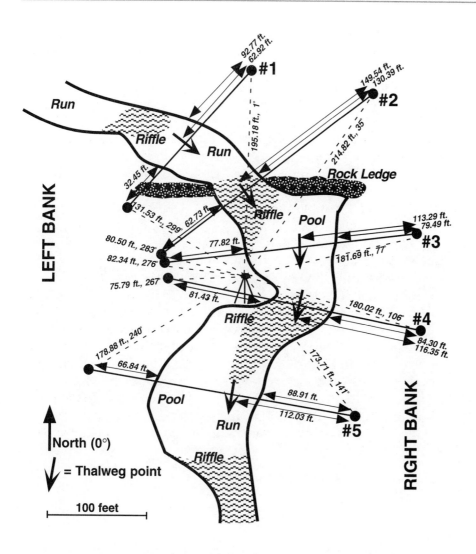

Figure 6.2 Sketch of a study site with notes and field measurements from a survey level and ruled tape. Recorded on this sketch are distances and angles off North for the endpoints of transects, and distances from the transect endpoints to the water edge and thalweg on each bank. Habitat features and other notes can be drawn on the sketch to complete a scale site map. A survey level is located in the middle of the illustration.

site sketch (Figure 6.2). The distance from one endpoint to the thalweg (point of greatest depth on a cross section), and the distances from each transect endpoint to the stream edges are measured using tape measures and are recorded on each transect. Finally, the site is mapped on graph paper in the office or using a computer drafting program. See Gordon et al. (1992), Harrelson et al. (1994), or an introductory manual on surveying or basic survey instrument techniques. Five or six transects should be adequate for developing a site map, and a subset of transects can be surveyed when more transects are used for cross section measurements. In such a case, use the first, last, and three or more intermediate transects.

■ **Develop a longitudinal profile for the site.** A longitudinal (upstream–downstream) profile provides a view of the elevation change in the water surface and stream bottom through an assessment site. The profile should be based on the thalweg points on all transects. A site map provides the distances between the thalweg points of all or some transects. A subset of about five transects will provide an adequate basis for a longitudinal profile if all transects are not surveyed. Elevations for the water surface and stream bottom at the thalweg points are not available from the site map. To obtain the elevations, position a survey level so that the uppermost transect is visible and the instrument is higher than the water surface of this transect. Then, measure the elevations of the water surface and stream bottom using a level rod positioned at the thalweg point on each mapped transect as shown in Figure 6.3. The elevations from the level readings will increase moving downstream because the measurements are distances below the survey level height. Subtract all these values from an arbitrary elevation like 100 feet (survey level height) so the largest numbers are at the highest elevations. Make a longitudinal site plot (see Figure 6.4) using the final elevation values and distances between thalweg points from a scale site map (Figure 6.2). Figure 6.4 shows the pattern of elevation change at a site and the water surface and stream bottom slopes that are based on only the highest and lowest elevations in a slope formula:

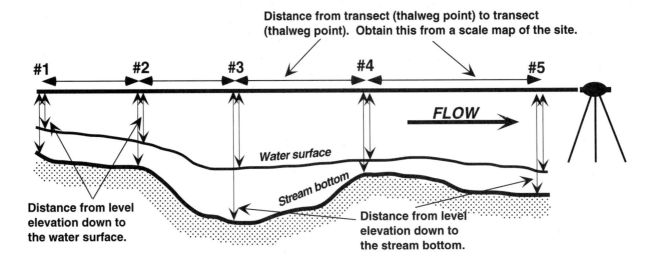

Figure 6.3   A diagram of longitudinal profile measurements using a survey level shown on the right. On the thalweg point of each transect, record the distance from the height of the survey level down to the water surface and stream bottom.

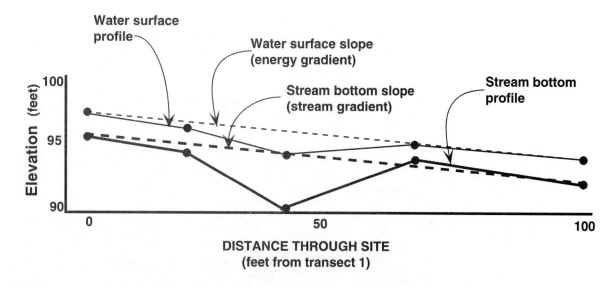

Figure 6.4   A longitudinal profile plot of the study site based on distance and elevation data from survey work described in Figure 6.3. Average water and stream bottom gradients are shown. The water surface slope is used as an estimate of the energy gradient in the Manning equation, and the stream bottom gradient is usually regarded as the slope of the stream in the site. The two slopes become equivalent at bankfull discharge and higher.

$$\text{Percent slope} = \text{Rise/run} \times 100$$

Where the rise/run value is: $\dfrac{\text{highest elevation} - \text{lowest elevation}}{\text{distance between elevation points}}$.

All measurements in the computation should be in the same units (meters or feet). Elevation change is also reported as gradient using unit per unit change; for example, feet per feet (or meters).

- **Complete final calculations and estimates.** Using the data from the site survey and a scale site map, compute the following basic descriptors of the assessment site:

    - Mean wet stream width: average of transect widths with water.

    - Mean bankfull width: average of bankfull channel widths.

    - Wetted perimeter: average of transect wetted perimeter measurements.

    - Stream depth: average of water depth measurements.

    - Maximum bankfull depth: the largest measurement obtained at the site.

    - Total reach area: measure the area (planimeter or computer) of the stream on the site map, or compute an estimate as the product of site length times mean stream width.

- Cross section area: compute an estimate for each transect as the product of mean depth times wet stream width, and then average transect cross-section areas for a mean site estimate.

- Water surface slope (energy gradient) and stream bottom slope (stream gradient), and stream gradient: computation described above.

- Channel roughness (Manning's *n*): see Box 6.1.

6.4 Notes

Harrelson et al. (1994) provides good instruction in the use of surveying equipment. This manual is available free from the U.S. Forest Service Stream Systems Technology Center (http://www.stream.fs.fed.us/ or telephone 970-498-1731).

Distances for cross-sectional and longitudinal profile surveys should be measured to 0.1 ft (0.03 m) and elevations should be measured to 0.01 ft (0.003 m).

Barnes (1967) provides stream site photographs, channel data, plan sketches, and cross section plots to visually estimate roughness.

Benchmarks are elevation reference points for transect and site surveys. Permanent basemarks can be a boulder, a tree spike, or a rebar (concrete reinforcing iron bar) well secured in the ground. Large embedded boulders can be marked with spray paint, a lightly chiseled X, a drilled hole with a bolt, or a combination of these marks. A tree spike monument can be made by driving a 40–80 penny spike partially into the base of a large tree that has stable roots. A rebar monument can be made by driving a 3–4 ft (90–120 cm) by 0.5 in (1–1.5 cm) diameter rebar into the ground to within 1–1.5 cm of the ground surface. Cover the rebar with a plastic cap or tag it with an aluminum survey marker tag. When repeated site surveys are not expected, a temporary benchmark can be any object that will remain stationary during fieldwork such as a flat rock, brick, or wooden stake.

The bankfull level of a stream is often hard to identify but this can be done reliably with experience interpreting indicators such as water marks or scour lines and changes in vegetation, slope, and bank materials. Consult detailed hydrology texts for guidance (Gordon et al. 1992; Rosgen 1996).

Transect measurements go with substrate, discharge, cover, velocity, bank condition; see corresponding chapters for more information.

Survey equipment is developing rapidly and we expect that laser devices and global positioning systems equipment will become widely available and commonly used in the next few years.

Box 6.1 Estimating channel roughness.

The Manning's equation results in a value (n) that explains the resistance to water flow caused by the stream channel. Manning's n values range from about 0.020 to 0.075 for large streams and rivers (Barnes 1967). High values are associated with channels that have more large rock, wood debris, and other flow-resisting material. The Manning's equation is:

$$n = \frac{1.486 R^{2/3} S^{1/2}}{v}$$

R = the hydraulic radius (ft) which is computed as the cross section area divided by wetted perimeter (can use average site values)
S = energy gradient (ft/ft) or water surface slope
v = the mean stream velocity (ft/s) which can be computed as the stream discharge divided by average cross section area

Example data and calculations for Cascadilla Creek near Ithaca, New York:

Transect	Mean depth (ft)	Stream width (ft)	Cross section area (ft²)	Wetted perimeter (ft)	Hydraulic radius (ft)
1	0.64	24	15.36	25.8	0.60
2	0.73	14	10.22	15.5	0.66
3	1.80	24	43.20	27.6	1.57
4	1.40	23	32.20	25.8	1.25
5	1.30	26	33.80	28.6	1.18
Means			26.96		1.052

Water surface slope or energy gradient:
0.35 feet drop over 203.42 feet distance = 0.0017

Stream discharge at the time of survey = 23 ft³/s

Mean stream velocity: $\dfrac{23\,\text{ft}^3/\text{s}}{26.96\,\text{ft}^2} = 0.85\,\text{ft/s}$

Manning's n calculation:

$$n = \frac{1.486(1.05^{2/3})(0.0017^{1/2})}{0.85} \qquad n = \frac{1.486(1.03)(0.041)}{0.85}$$

NOTE: Replace the coefficient 1.486 with 1.0 if using metric units.

Classification of Streams and Reaches

7

Kristin K. Arend

7.1 Introduction

7.1.1 Background

Stream channels form and are maintained by the interaction of streamflow and sediment regimes in a process that yields consistent average channel shape and size (Dunne and Leopold 1978). A reach is a section of a stream at least 20 times longer than its average channel width (Flosi and Reynolds 1994) that maintains homogenous channel morphology, flow, and physical, chemical, and biological characteristics. Streams and reaches are typically classified into types based on valley form, channel width, average depth and velocity, mean discharge, gradient, roughness of channel materials, sediment load and sizes, channel entrenchment, sinuosity, and other attributes (Rosgen 1994; Maxwell et al. 1995; Moore et al. 1995). Changes in land use or climate will initiate natural alterations in channel pattern, stream characteristics, and usually the stream or reach type.

Streams or segments of streams are often classified at one of three levels: broad classification of the entire stream, classification of a particular reach within the stream, or classification of macrohabitat within a reach. This chapter presents techniques for broad and reach classification; techniques for macrohabitat classification are presented in Chapter 8. Broad classification uses morphological criteria to characterize stream distribution within a watershed or region (Rosgen 1996). Identifying and describing stream reaches with a well-developed classification system provides a common frame of reference. The objectives for classifying stream reaches are to consistently characterize channel types, make comparisons among stream channels, and partition physical habitat among and within streams (Harrelson et al. 1994).

A comprehensive classification system provides insight into the formation and maintenance of stream channel attributes. Similar and different reaches within and between streams can then be compared. Furthermore, once the characteristics of representative reach types are known, they can be extrapolated to reaches of the same type for which measurements of many properties have not been made. This information could serve as a baseline for assessing a stream's current condition, estimating its probable form, monitoring or predicting the changes it may undergo over time and under different conditions, and developing sound restoration and management projects (Rosgen 1994; Maxwell et al. 1995). For example, knowledge of reach types can be useful when selecting fish habitat improvement projects to maintain the stability and function of the stream (Rosgen 1994).

7.1.2 Selection of Techniques

The three classifications presented here are based on channel geomorphology and the techniques link channel attributes and the surrounding landform. Classification systems developed by David Rosgen (1994, 1996), Galay et al. (1973), and Montgomery and Buffington (1983) were selected for this manual on the basis of applicability, practicality, and use by fisheries agencies. The techniques have been slightly modified to incorporate missing geomorphic or landform information, and to provide instructions for new users who lack experience making rapid judgments about classification.

The Rosgen technique (Rosgen 1994, 1996) is used by a number of state and federal agencies (e.g., the California Department of Fish and Game [Flosi and Reynolds 1994], Bureau of Land Management [Armantrout 1996]). This classification technique is based on quantitative channel morphology indices, and results in objective and consistent identification of stream types. The technique is suitable for a range of assessment objectives because streams can be classified to any of four levels of resolution. We present two of the four levels. Level I classification identifies stream types and will be most accurate when the user has experience interpreting maps and photographs and is familiar with the drainage basin being studied. Level II classification identifies reach types within each stream type. Level II classification requires field work, but measurements can be extrapolated from one stream reach to another of the same type, thereby covering a larger area but with a minimal increase in workload.

The classification technique of Galay et al. (1973) has not been widely used; however, it is a unique and practical classification system in which a checklist is used to document stream and reach types. Topographic maps and aerial photographs are used with this technique, which can be conducted entirely in an office. It is the least time consuming and expensive of the three techniques presented here. It is, however, the least rigorous technique because data quality depends on the accuracy and age of the maps and field verification is not required. This technique is not applicable to the headwaters of rivers.

The bed form technique, first proposed by Montgomery and Buffington (1983), is used regularly (e.g., the U.S. Forest Service [Maxwell et al. 1995]); it integrates well with channel geomorphic classification (see Chapter 8). This technique is comprehensive despite being less complex than the Rosgen technique. Classification is based on information from maps and photographs, but a site visit is required to verify reach boundaries and their classifications. Although more rigorous than the Galay technique, it too relies on the accuracy of the maps and photographs. Also, this technique does not resolve finer-scale bed forms (e.g., channel geomorphic units such as pools and riffles) and reach transitions in many streams (Bisson and Montgomery 1996).

7.2 Rosgen Technique

7.2.1 Rationale

The Rosgen stream classification technique can be used to identify an entire stream or a reach, and the technique is based on valley and channel morphology. The technique presented here is a modification of the first two levels of Rosgen's (1994, 1996) hierarchical system. Rosgen's levels III and IV involve precise measurement of reach properties to verify classification at levels I or II. We judged techniques for level III and IV classification are beyond the needs for most fisheries agency habitat assessments and, therefore, did not include them in this manual. The following technique is applicable to both ephemeral and perennial reaches: stream types are determined at points where the channel geometry is not affected by outside influences (e.g., road embankments, rip-rap, landslides, tributaries). A reach type may range in length from 20 meters to several kilometers, but should be at least two meander widths (or 20 bankfull channel widths) in length. Level I classification is based on work with maps and aerial photographs, but some field observations (e.g., the location of reach transitions and the presence of interesting features) and measurements (e.g., channel depth and bankfull elevation) are required. Level II classification depends on fieldwork.

Level I classification is necessarily broad, and integrates the landform and fluvial features of valley morphology with channel relief, pattern, shape, and dimension. Stream types are classified using (1) generalized descriptions of longitudinal profiles, valley and channel cross-section morphologies, and plan-view morphologies, (2) ranges for measurements of slope, entrenchment ratio, width-to-depth ratio, and sinuosity, and (3) descriptions of the landform, soils, and other features (Figure 7.1). Definitions and characteristics used for classifications are provided in Table 7.1. Using these criteria, the following nine stream types are identified: Aa+, A, B, C, D, DA, E, F, and G. For an individual stream type, the esti-

Stream type	General description	Longitudinal profile (slope)	Cross section	Plan view morphology	Landform, soils, features
Aa+	Very steep; deeply entrenched; debris transport; torrent	>0.10	ER <1.4 W:D <12	Sinuosity 1.0–1.1	Very high relief; erosional, bedrock, or depositional features; debris flow potential; deeply entrenched; vertical steps with deep scour pools; waterfalls
A	Steep, entrenched, cascading, step–pool; high energy and debris transport, depositional soils; very stable if bedrock or boulder dominated	0.04–0.10	ER <1.4 W:D <12	Sinuosity 1.0–1.2	High relief; erosional or depositional and bedrock forms; entrenched and confined; cascading reaches; frequently spaced, deep pools; step–pool bed morphology
B	Moderately entrenched, moderate gradient; riffle dominated; infrequently spaced pools; very stable plan and profile; stable banks	0.02–0.039	ER 1.4–2.2 W:D >12	Sinuosity >1.2	Moderate relief, colluvial deposition, and structural; moderate entrenchment and W:D ratio; narrow, gently sloping valleys; rapids predominate with scour pools
C	Low gradient; meandering riffle–pool; alluvial; broad, well-defined floodplains	<0.02	ER >1.2 W:D >12	Sinuosity >1.4	Broad valleys with terraces in association with floodplains; alluvial soils; slightly entrenched; well-defined meandering; riffle–pool bed morphology
D	Braided; longitudinal and transverse bars; very wide; eroding banks	<0.04	ER n/a W:D >40	Sinuosity n/a	Broad valleys; alluvium, steeper fans; glacial debris and depositional features; active lateral adjustment; abundance of sediment supply; convergence or divergence bed features; aggradational processes; high bedload and bank erosion
DA	Anastomosing; narrow, deep; extensive, well-vegetated floodplains and associated wetlands; gentle relief; highly variable sinuosities and W:D ratios; very stable banks	<0.005	ER >2.2 W:D highly variable	Sinuosity highly variable	Valleys broad, low gradient with fine alluvium or lacustrine soils; anastomosed; fine deposition; well-vegetated bars are laterally stable; broad wetland floodplains; very low bedload; high wash load sediment
E	Low gradient; meandering; riffle–pool; low W:D ratio; little deposition; very efficient and stable; high meander width ratio	<0.02	ER >2.2 W:D <12	Sinuosity >1.5	Broad valley or meadows; alluvial materials with floodplains; highly sinuous; stable, well-vegetated banks; riffle–pool morphology; very low W:D ratios
F	Entrenched; meandering; riffle–pool; low gradient; high W:D ratio	<0.02	ER <1.4 W:D >12	Sinuosity >1.4	Entrenched in highly weathered material; gentle gradients; high W:D ratio; meandering; laterally unstable with high bank erosion rates; riffle–pool morphology
G	Entrenched "gully"; step pool; low W:D ratio; moderate gradients	0.02–0.039	ER <1.4 W:D <12	Sinuosity >1.2	Gullies; step–pool morphology; moderate slopes; low W:D ratio; narrow valleys or deeply incised in alluvial or colluvial materials; unstable with grade control problems and high bank erosion rates

Figure 7.1   Guidelines for the Rosgen level II reach type classification. Modified from Rosgen (1996). ER = entrenchment ratio, W:D = width-to-depth ratio.

Table 7.1   Level I stream type classification criteria for the Rosgen technique.

Description	Criteria	Characteristics

Longitudinal profile
channel morphology
(slope and bed features)
	slope
	  >10%
	  4–10%
	  <4%
	  <2%
	  <0.5%
	
	bed features
	  scour pool
	  step–pool
	  riffle–pool
		combination of slope and bed feature
		spacing of bed features
		influence of scour and deposition

Cross section morphology
shape of the streambed,
floodplain, and terraces
	narrow, deep streams
	wide, shallow streams
		degree of channel incision within the
		  parent valley
		location and extent of floodplains
		occurrence and position of terraces
		presence of colluvial slopes
		presence of structural control features
		degree of channel entrenchment
		overall valley versus channel macro-
		  dimensions

Plan-view morphology plan-view of the river pattern as it flows through the valley	relatively straight low sinuosity meandering tortuously meandering complex: multiple, braided, anastomosed	

mated or measured value of each classification criterion must fall within a specified range. However, the general geomorphologic characterization of a stream type may remain unaltered if there is only a minor inconsistency in criteria values.

Level II classification refines the level I stream types by identifying reaches nested within each of the nine level I categories. In level II, a stream type is verified by field measurements of entrenchment ratio, width-to-depth ratio, and sinuosity. Then, reaches are further classified using field measurements of the dominant channel material and stream slope. Bed and bank materials determine the form, plan, and profile of a stream, and these attributes are used in the Rosgen classification. Water surface slope also influences a channel's morphology and its sediment, hydraulic, and biological function, and this attribute is directly used in the level II classification. Bankfull width and mean bankfull depth are also measured for accurate calculations of entrenchment ratio and width-to-depth ratio. A level II reach type is designated by adding a number and sometimes a lowercase letter to the level I stream type designation (Table 7.2). Fieldwork for level I and level II classification can be conducted simultaneously.

Table 7.2   Guidelines for Rosgen's level II reach type classification. Modified from Rosgen 1996.

Stream type	Slope range	Channel material					
		Bedrock	Boulder	Cobble	Gravel	Sand	Silt or clay
A	>0.10	A1a+	A2a+	A3a+	A4a+	A5a+	A6a+
	0.04–0.099	A1	A2	A3	A4	A5	A6
	0.04–0.099	B1a	B2a	B3a	B4a	B5a	B6a
B	0.02–0.039	B1	B2	B3	B4	B5	B6
	<0.02	B1c	B2c	B3c	B4c	B5c	B6c
	0.02–0.039	C1b	C2b	C3b	C4b	C5b	C6b
C	0.001–0.02	C1	C2	C3	C4	C5	C6
	<0.001	C1c–	C2c–	C3c–	C4c–	C5c–	C6c–
	0.02–0.039	n/a	n/a	D3b	D4b	D5b	D6b
D	0.001–0.02	n/a	n/a	D3	D4	D4	D6
	<0.001	n/a	n/a	n/a	D4c–	D5c–	D6c–
DA	<0.005	n/a	n/a	n/a	DA4	DA5	DA6
E	0.02–0.039	n/a	n/a	E3b	E4b	E5b	E6b
	<0.02	n/a	n/a	E3	E4	E5	E6
F	0.02–0.039	F1b	F2b	F3b	F4b	F5b	F6b
	<0.02	F1	F2	F3	F4	F5	F6
G	0.02–0.039	G1	G2	G3	G4	G5	G6
	<0.02	G1c	G2c	G3c	G4c	G5c	G6c

7.2.2 Preparation

Level I

▶ Become familiar with stadiometers (map measurer) and planimeters.

▶ Acquire U.S. Geological Survey (USGS) topographic maps at 1:24,000 scale, land cover maps, watershed maps, a geologic map at 1:250,000 scale, soil or glacial maps (Duff et al. 1989).

▶ Acquire aerial photographs: Bisson and Montgomery (1996) suggest using low altitude photographs at the 1:12,000 scale or larger; Duff et al. (1989) suggest using photographs with a minimum scale of 1:2,000. Photographs should be taken when streams are at a base flow.

▶ Assemble cross-section (transect) profiling equipment (see Chapter 6 for a list).

▶ Prepare a data recording sheet.

Level II

▶ Complete preparation for level I.

▶ Obtain permission to work on private land, if required.

7.2.3 Procedures

Level I

▪ **Delineation of valley types and landforms.** Overlay the drainage system of interest on a topographic map that has landforms identified (e.g., alluvial fans, glacial or fluvial terraces, floodplains, hanging valleys, other erosional or depositional features). Then, determine the elevation of terraces with respect to the elevations of the valley floor, using topographic elevation lines on the maps and field observations when needed.

▪ **Longitudinal profile (slope).** Use a stadiometer and a topographic map to measure the length of the main channel (L_c) from the outlet to the basin divide uphill of the most upstream point on the map. Identify the main channel at each bifurcation as the fork with the largest drainage area or the longest watercourse. Then, determine the upstream end of the channel by extending the main channel from the end of the mapped representation of the stream to the basin divide. Convert stadiometer units to kilometers using the map legend and a calculator. Measure elevation above mean sea level of the streambed at distances (m) 10% (E_{10}) and 85% (E_{85}) along the main channel from the outlet (see Chapter 6 for elevation procedure). Finally, calculate slope (m/km) as the change in elevation over the length of the main channel from the 10% and 85% points:

$$S_c = (E_{85} - E_{10})/0.75L_c$$

▪ **Bed features** (e.g., pools, riffles, rapids). Infer bed features from general slope categories estimated from topographic maps and from aerial photographs taken at base flow. Some field reconnaissance may be needed to verify bed features. Use the slope estimates and the criteria in Table 7.1 to characterize the longitudinal profile of the stream.

▪ **Cross-section morphology.** Entrenchment ratio is estimated as the typical flood width divided by bankfull channel width. The bankfull stage is the height of water reached at flows primarily responsible for channel formation (Dunne and Leopold 1978). It is also the water height when the stream channel is filled to the top of the banks, equal to the floodplain surface (Gordon et al. 1992). Bankfull discharge, or the stream volume at bankfull stage, is determined in the field by: (1) the elevation of the top of the highest depositional features such as point and central bars, (2) a change in the size distribution of substrate or bank particles, (3) a break in the slope of the banks, (4) stains on rocks, and (5) root hairs exposed below an intact soil layer (Rosgen 1996). Rosgen defines the typical flood width (i.e., flood prone area) as the elevation corresponding to twice the maximum depth of the bankfull channel, which usually includes the active floodplain and low terrace. If available, refer to a valley profile or cross-section profile for the reach that extends beyond the bankfull to the high flood level. Alternatively, make plots at representative reaches as described in Chapter 6, if cross-section profile plots are not available. Visually compare the cross section of the reach with Figure 7.2 to classify the reach as entrenched, moderately entrenched, or slightly entrenched.

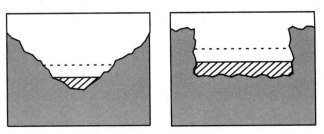

Entrenched (ratio: 1.0–1.4)

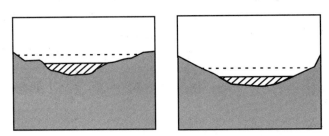

Moderately entrenched (ratio: 1.41–2.2)

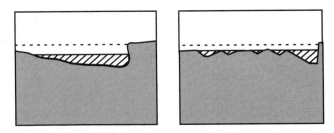

Slightly entrenched (ratio: >2.2)

- - - - - - - - - - channel width at typical flood

Figure 7.2   Example stream cross sections showing different entrenchment ratios with classification criteria from Rosgen (1996).

■ **Cross section morphology.** Stream width-to-depth ratio (W:D) at bankfull discharge. Measure bankfull channel width and mean depth following the procedure outlined in Chapter 6 at representative reaches along the stream. Divide the bankfull channel width by the mean channel depth to calculate the W:D value; see Figure 7.1 for interpretation criteria.

■ **Plan-view morphology.** Sinuosity (P) is estimated as the ratio of stream channel length to basin length. Use a metric ruler to measure the length (cm) of the basin (L_B) as the straight-line distance from the outlet to the point on the basin divide used to determine the main channel length (L_C). Convert the length to kilometers using the map legend and measure the length of the stream channel as described above for longitudinal profile (slope). Finally, calculate the sinuosity ratio as:

$$\text{Sinuosity } P = L_C / L_B$$

Refer to Table 7.3 for criteria used to interpret the sinuosity ratio.

■ **Stream classification.** Referring to the Rosgen level I classification criteria in Table 7.1, identify the most appropriate stream type shown and described in Figure 7.1.

Table 7.3   Rosgen level II measurements and interpretation criteria.

Criterion	Estimated or measured value	Interpretation
W:D ratio[a]	<12	low
	>12	moderate–high
Sinuosity[a]	<1.2	low
	>1.2	moderate
	>1.4	high
	>1.5	very high
Entrenchment ratio	1–1.4	entrenched
	1.41–2.2	moderately entrenched
	>2.2	slightly entrenched
Channel material	≥50.8 cm	large boulder
	25.4–50.8	small boulder
	6.35–25.4	cobble
	0.20–6.35	gravel
	0.062–2.0	sand
	<0.062	silt or clay

[a]Ratios for W:D ratio can vary by ±2.0 units; ratios for sinuosity and entrenchment ratio can vary by ±0.2 units.

Level II

■ **Slope.** Measure water surface elevation along the longitudinal profile of the channel using the protocol described in Chapter 6. Measure the water surface elevation at the upstream end of two consecutive features of the same type (e.g., the top of one riffle and the top of the closest, downstream or upstream riffle). Then, calculate the vertical height change for that section of stream as follows:

Vertical drop = (elevation of upstream feature) −
              (elevation of downstream feature) .

Repeat the elevation measurements until a length of reach has been covered that is at least 20 bankfull channel widths or two meander widths. Sum the vertical drops of the sections to compute the overall vertical drop of the reach (the difference between the elevation measured for the most upstream bed feature and that measured for the most downstream bed feature). Next measure the length (m) of the entire stream reach covered as described in Chapter 6. Finally, calculate the percent stream slope as:

Slope (%) = (vertical height/reach length) × 100.

■ **Entrenchment ratio.** Follow the protocol described above for level I classification and refer to Table 7.3 for interpretation criteria.

■ **Width-to-depth ratio.** Using the procedure described in Chapter 6, measure bankfull channel width and mean channel depth on six transects within the reach and refer to Table 7.3 for interpretation criteria.

■ **Sinuosity.** Follow the protocol described above for level I classification and refer to Table 7.3 for interpretation criteria.

■ **Channel material.** Characterize the reach substrate using the pebble count technique described in Chapter 9. Identify the median particle diameter (i.e., D-50 index diameters) using a cumulative size frequency plot (particle diameter for the 50 percentile point) described in Chapter 9 or by ranking the particles by size to find the middle observation. Alternatively, a histogram of material types (Table 7.3) can be used to determine the dominant particle size (i.e., the particle size having the greatest number of observations).

■ **Final stream reach classification.** The level II field measurements are used to guide the level I stream classification. Using all the information, and the classification guidance in Tables 7.1 and 7.3, select the most appropriate stream type from Figure 7.1. The stream type designation can be refined with the classification information on stream slope and channel material in Table 7.2.

7.2.4 Notes

The stream and reach classification criteria included in hierarchical levels I–IV are directly related to the pattern, probable state, and stability of the stream; therefore, it is possible to interpret energy distribution and modes of adjustment (vertical, lateral, or both) for each stream type. For example, the width-to-depth ratio is an accurate predictor of the most probable state of a stream's channel pattern and a rapid and reliable indicator of channel instability (Rosgen 1996).

Rosgen (1996) provides guidelines for the appropriateness and effectiveness of management activities (e.g., construction of fish habitat improvement structures) based on the stream type. A table summarizing each stream type's sensitivity to disturbance, recovery potential, sediment supply, streambank erosion potential, and vegetation controlling influence provides useful information to managers who make decisions about restoration, forestry, mining, or disturbance activities. Information collected about reach properties (e.g., dominant channel materials) can be used to interpret biological function and stability within the river (Rosgen 1994).

7.3   Galay System

7.3.1 Rationale

Galay et al. (1973) introduced a technique for stream classification based on geomorphic setting and dominant channel processes. Classification criteria include: (1) major geomorphic setting (e.g., alluvial plains, deltas, alluvial fans, irregular bedrock channels), (2) degree of valley confinement of the river, (3) river channel pattern (i.e., sinuosity), (4) channel bars, (5) islands, (6) stability of the valley wall, and (7) special features. The Galay technique relies entirely on the use of maps and aerial photographs. Galay et al. (1973) suggest that additional classification criteria could be incorporated into the method. As described here, the classification is applicable to a variety of rivers and streams excluding headwaters.

7.3.2 Preparation

▶ Acquire USGS topographic maps at 1:24,000 scale, land cover maps, a geologic map at 1:250,000 scale, and soil or glacial maps (Duff et al. 1989).

▶ Acquire aerial photographs: Bisson and Montgomery (1996) suggest using low altitude photos at the 1:12,000 scale or larger; Duff et al. (1989) suggest using photographs with a minimum scale of 1:2,000. Photographs should be taken at base flow.

7.3.3 Procedures

■ Determine if the river geomorphic setting is valley, alluvial plain, delta, alluvial fan, or irregular bedrock channels. See the glossary by Armantrout (1998) for definitions of these terms.

■ Use topographic maps and aerial photographs to determine to what extent the river is confined to the valley for valley reaches only. Assign stream reaches to one of the entrenchment categories described in Table 7.4; a combination of categories is possible within a single stream.

■ Determine the river channel pattern (sinuosity) by referring to aerial photographs and then assigning the stream reach to one of the channel pattern categories described in Table 7.4. Categories apply to the channel pattern at low flow stage, the conditions under which most maps and aerial photographs are taken.

■ Identify channel bars (i.e., usually unvegetated channel deposits) in the reach by referring to aerial photographs and Table 7.4.

■ Identify islands in the reach by examining aerial photographs and categories in Table 7.4. Islands are more permanent features than channel bars because islands typically remain above the water level at bankfull flows and have well-established vegetation.

■ After reviewing aerial photographs, tentatively classify the valley wall of the reach as stable, some slumping, or extensive slumping.

■ Describe special features, especially those that may have an effect on the appearance of the river channel (e.g., bedrock outcrops, boulder rapids, log jams, permafrost effects, river engineering works).

■ Record classification information from the available choices in Table 7.5.

7.3.4 Notes

The Galay technique could incorporate other river and stream features such as: (1) the magnitude and distribution of land surface runoff (e.g., seasonal runoff, natural storage), (2) the extent to which ice shapes the channel, (3) channel stability relative to bank and bed materials, and (4) channel geometry, bed forms, rates of channel shift, rates of degradation and aggradation, and transport rates of bed load.

Table 7.4 Galay et al. technique for stream classification based on geomorphic setting and dominant channel processes.

Classification criteria	Description
Entrenchment	
Entrenched channel	Channel bordered on either side by banks higher than the highest flood level Is either actively degrading or has been doing so in the past
Partly entrenched channel	Channel bordered occasionally by discontinuous segments of floodplain It is common to have a combination of degradation with some lateral shifting and floodplain construction
Confined channel	Channel is either stable (vertically) or aggrading and the valley floor is predominantly a floodplain The channel alternately impinges on the left and right valley walls because the valley is far too narrow for the proper development of the river's meander pattern
Partly confined channel	Channel is confined by valley walls, fans, or slumps over short reaches, but there is sufficient room on the valley floodplain for the full development of some meanders
Channel pattern	
Straight channel	Very little curvature Usually due to structural controls; however, straight reaches occur in extremely flat channels in deltaic regions
Regular meanders	Repeatable meandering pattern Confined meanders typically have exceptional regularity
Tortuous meanders	Loops have a variety of shapes Characteristic feature: angle between the valley axis and the channel at cross-overs is frequently greater than 90° Prerequisites for development: low valley slope and relatively resistant floodplain deposits Also found in entrenched channels
Irregular meanders	Meander loops are discontinuous
Irregular channel	Abrupt changes in flow direction or sudden expansions and constrictions
Channel bars	
Point bars	Location: the inside of a river bend Process: become increasingly integrated into the active floodplain at the inside of the bend, as bank erosion at the outside of meander bends causes the river to shift laterally
Side bars	Location: adjacent to banks Usually present in a channel with straight or irregular patterns
Mid-channel bars	Take on a variety of appearances
Diagonal bars	Ridges common in gravel-bed channels Location: extend across part of a channel Water flow spills across the bar in the form of a riffle or small rapid

Table 7.4   Continued.

Classification criteria	Description
Islands	
Occasional islands	Infrequent Don't overlap
Frequent islands	Are prominent within the channel Occasionally overlap
Split channel	Continuous overlap of islands forming two or three channels over most of the reach
Braided channel	Islands generally overlap forming more than two flow channels Islands are unstable and resemble mid-channel bars There is a constant transition from channels with frequent mid-channel bars to truly braided channels

Notes:

(1) Use the term floodplain to describe the surface built up by the present river through lateral accretion and aggradation.
(2) It may not be possible to clearly distinguish low terraces and active floodplains without conducting field work; however, under extreme conditions, low terraces may be subject to flooding.

7.4 Bed Form System

7.4.1 Rationale

The Montgomery and Buffington (1983) classification technique identifies stream reaches as one of three kinds of valley reaches: colluvial, alluvial, or bedrock. As with the previous two techniques, the classification criteria are based on entrenchment, slope, and sinuosity. Maps and aerial photographs are used to identify reach boundaries by estimating stream gradients, degree of valley confinement, channel meander patterns, and significant changes in the predominant rock type. Although this technique can be completed in an office, a site visit is strongly recommended to verify the reach boundaries identified from the maps and photographs.

Classification of a valley reach is based on dominant types of sediment input and transport processes (Bisson and Montgomery 1996). In colluvial valleys, landslides from adjacent hillslopes deliver sediment and organic matter to the valley floor; whereas, in alluvial valleys, streamflow transports sediment along the valley floor (Bisson and Montgomery 1996). Bedrock valleys have little soil (Bisson and Montgomery 1996). Only colluvial reaches are found within colluvial valley segments and only bedrock reaches are found within bedrock valley segments. However, a reach in an alluvial valley segment can be identified as braided, regime, pool–riffle, plane-bed, step-pool, or cascade. The stream is separated into reaches based on average gradient and apparent degree of valley confinement. Changes in slope indicate where reach boundaries may

Table 7.5   River classification categories of Galay et al. (1973) that are evident from maps and aerial photographs. Select the combination of classes from those listed here where multiple entries in a column represent possible choices.

Landform	River channel pattern	Channel bars	Islands	Valley wall stability
Alluvial floodplain	Straight Regular meander Tortuous meander Irregular meander Irregular channel	Point Side Side, mid-channel, diagonal	Frequent, split, braided	Stable, minor slump, extensive slump Stable, minor slump, extensive slump Stable, minor slump, extensive slump Stable, minor slump, extensive slump Stable, minor slump, extensive slump
Delta	Straight Regular meander Tortuous meander Irregular meander Irregular channel	Point Side Point, mid-channel, side, diagonal	Occasional, frequent, split, braided	Stable, minor slump, extensive slump Stable, minor slump, extensive slump Stable, minor slump, extensive slump Stable, minor slump, extensive slump Stable, minor slump, extensive slump
Alluvial fan	Straight Regular meander Tortuous meander Irregular meander Irregular channel	Point Side Point, mid-channel, side, diagonal	Occasional, frequent, split, braided	Stable, minor slump, extensive slump Stable, minor slump, extensive slump Stable, minor slump, extensive slump Stable, minor slump, extensive slump Stable, minor slump, extensive slump
Bedrock channel	Straight Regular meander Tortuous meander Irregular meander Irregular channel	Point, mid-channel, side, diagonal Point, mid-channel, side, diagonal Point, mid-channel, side, diagonal Point, mid-channel, side, diagonal	Occasional, frequent, split, braided Occasional, frequent, split, braided Occasional, frequent, split, braided Occasional, frequent, split, braided	Stable, minor slump, extensive slump Stable, minor slump, extensive slump Stable, minor slump, extensive slump Stable, minor slump, extensive slump
Valley				
entrenched channel	Straight Regular meander Tortuous meander Irregular meander Irregular channel	Point Side Mid-channel, side, diagonal	Split, braided Split, braided Frequent, split, braided Split, braided Split, braided	
partly entrenched	Straight Regular meander Tortuous meander Irregular meander Irregular channel	Point Side Mid-channel, side, diagonal	Frequent, split, braided	
confined channel	Straight Regular meander Tortuous meander Irregular meander Irregular channel	Point Side Mid-channel, side, diagonal	Frequent, split, braided	
partly confined channel	Straight Regular meander Tortuous meander Irregular meander Irregular channel	Point Side Mid-channel, side, diagonal	Frequent, split, braided	

exist. Use maps and photographs to estimate elevation, channel width, valley floor width, and channel length to approximate slope and confinement. Also use aerial photographs, geological maps, and soils maps to accurately locate changes in channel shape and boundaries between geological formations. Criteria are broken into seven categories: (1) predominant bed material, (2) bedform pattern (sinuosity), (3) dominant roughness elements, (4) dominant sediment sources, (5) typical slope, (6) typical confinement, and (7) pool spacing. Table 7.6 defines each reach type according to these criteria.

Table 7.6 Characteristics of different types of stream reaches for bed form stream reach classification. From Bisson and Montgomery (1996).

Characteristics	Colluvial	Bedrock	Alluvial					
			Cascade	Step–pool	Plane–bed	Pool–riffle	Regime	Braided
Predominant bed material	Variable	Bedrock	Boulder	Cobble or boulder	Gravel or cobble	Gravel	Sand	Variable
Bedform pattern	Variable	Variable	None	Vertically oscillatory	None	Laterally oscillatory	Multilayered	Laterally oscillatory
Dominant roughness elements	Boulders, large woody debris	Streambed, banks	Boulders, banks	Bedforms (steps, pools), boulders, large woody debris, banks	Boulders and cobbles, banks	Bedforms (bars, pools), boulders and cobbles, large woody debris, sinuosity, banks	Sinuousity, bedforms (dunes, ripples, bars), banks	Bedforms (bars, pools)
Dominant sediment sources	Hilltops, debris flows	Fluvial, hillslope, debris flows	Fluvial, hillslope, debris flows	Fluvial, hillslope, debris flows	Fluvial, bank erosion, debris flows	Fluvial, bank erosion, inactive channels, debris flows	Fluvial, bank erosion, inactive channels	Fluvial, bank erosion, debris flows
Typical slope (%)	>20	Variable	8–30	4–8	1–4	0.1–2	<0.1	<3
Typical confinement	Strongly confined	Strongly confined	Strongly confined	Moderately confined	Variable	Unconfined	Unconfined	Unconfined
Pool spacing (channel widths)	Variable	Variable	<1	1–4	None	5–7	5–7	Variable

7.4.2 Preparation

▶ Obtain permission to survey on private land, if necessary.

▶ Select sites that allow for comparison of commonly occurring local reach types.

▶ Obtain low altitude aerial photographs at 1:12,000 scale or larger.

▶ Acquire topographic (1:24,000 scale), geological, and soils maps.

▶ Develop proficiency in the use of a stadiometer (map measurer), stereoscopic map reader, magnifying lens, or dissecting microscope.

▶ Collect 100-m and 30-m fiberglass tape; flagging; meter stick; optical, electronic, or sonic rangefinder; surveyor's rod or graduated wading staff (see Chapter 6).

7.4.3 Procedure

Office Procedures

■ Working with maps, construct a longitudinal profile of the stream channel from the stream mouth or confluence toward the headwaters. Measure the distance along the blue stream line using a stadiometer or a finely graduated ruler. Be sure to calibrate graduations of the stadiometer or ruler against the map scale. Record the elevation and distance from the downstream starting point each time a contour line intersects the stream line. Plot the longitudinal profile of the stream by labeling the vertical plot axis "Elevation (m)" and the horizontal axis "Distance from mouth (km)." The stream source should be nearest the vertical axis as shown in the example plot (Figure 7.3).

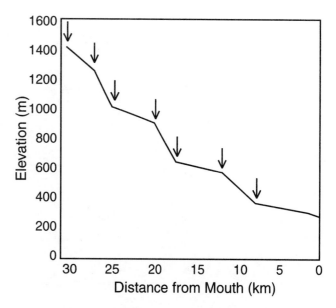

Figure 7.3 Example stream longitudinal profile with arrows indicating reach transitions.

- Identify reaches on the longitudinal profile by visually locating inflection points and marking them as seen in the example plot (Figure 7.3). The inflections are usually good indicators of reach transitions. Compute the average channel slope for each reach by measuring the elevations at both the upstream (E_u) and downstream (E_d) ends, then measure the reach length (L_r) as the distance between the downstream and upstream boundaries. To compute S or the average reach slope, use the equation:

$$S = \frac{E_u - E_d}{L_r} \ .$$

- Approximate the level of valley confinement in each reach by examining the shape of the contour lines intersecting the stream. Although the channel width will not be shown on most topographic maps, the general shape and width of the valley floor indicate valley confinement. Figure 7.4 provides examples of topographic maps that indicate the general extent of stream confinement. When possible, approximate the degree of confinement for the reach by examining aerial photographs of the stream segments identified on the topographic maps. Use a stereoscopic map reader, magnifying lens, or dissecting microscope to view the unvegetated channel and estimate the channel width. Estimate the width of the valley floor from the topographic maps. Compare the width of the valley floor with the width of the stream channel to approximate the degree of confinement as:

Strongly confined: valley floor width <2 channel widths;

Moderately confined: valley floor width = 2–4 channel widths;

Unconfined: valley floor width >4 channel widths.

- Consider whether the reach exhibits homogenous geological forms, dominant vegetation, soil composition, and climate. Compare average gradients and valley floor widths of each reach on the stream profile with geological, soils, vegetation, and climatological maps.

- Use boundaries evident on geological, soils, vegetation, and climatological maps to either verify the location of the reach boundaries or more accurately locate them.

- Finally, identify the reach type using the classification guidelines presented in Table 7.6.

Field Procedures

- Verify the accuracy of the reach type designation by inspecting the stream channel, adjacent valley floor, and hillslopes. Locate landmarks that indicate reach boundaries on maps if it is possible to get a panoramic view of the valley floor.

- Calibrate optical, electronic, or sonic rangefinders by measuring the distance between two points with a tape and adjusting the readings on the rangefinders to match the known distance. Use rangefinders and other survey equipment to measure attributes estimated from aerial photographs and topographic maps.

7.4.4 Notes

Maps may not provide very accurate information on sinuosity and channel braiding and they may not resolve key changes in stream gradient and valley confinement associated with reach transitions in small streams (Bisson and Montgomery 1996). Field measurements will be important in these cases. Also, the identification of finer-scale bed forms (e.g., channel geomorphic units such as pools and riffles) using aerial photographs may be difficult for many streams.

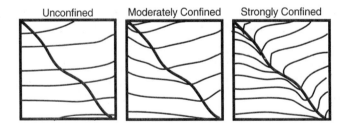

Figure 7.4 Example topographic map representations of streams considered to be unconfined, moderately confined, and unconfined.

Macrohabitat Identification

8

Kristin K. Arend

8.1 Introduction

8.1.1 Background

Macrohabitat identification is a method to efficiently describe, inventory, and assess streams for possible support of fisheries resources. A stream reach is divided into discrete habitats called channel geomorphic units (CGUs) which provide a framework for organizing and understanding habitat changes throughout a stream reach. The term CGUs is used throughout this chapter to convey the idea that macrohabitats are instream physical entities. Bed form, water velocity, the presence of flow control features, and other physical attributes form the basis for CGUs. Macrohabitat identification involves two steps: (1) determining the location and size of CGUs that compose a reach (henceforth called delineation); and (2) classifying the units into habitat types that are nested in levels of related groups and subgroups (henceforth called classification). The classification systems represent varying degrees of habitat resolution (i.e., the descriptive power of the CGU); therefore, the specific needs of an assessment can be met and compared across studies or cases (Hawkins et al. 1993).

Channel geomorphic units are relatively homogenous areas of a channel that differ in depth, velocity, and substrate characteristics from adjoining areas creating different habitat types in a stream channel. They are usually as long as the average wetted channel width or larger. Interactions between flow and streambed roughness are usually responsible for the creation of individual CGUs (Moore et al. 1995; Bisson and Montgomery 1996). They are easily recognized during periods of low flow in third-order and smaller streams; examples are different types of pools and riffles.

The physical characteristics of a stream are dependent upon the geological history and climate of a drainage basin, and watershed processes such as fluvial dynamics (Frissell et al. 1986; Poole et al. 1997). These characteristics determine both the type of reach (Chapter 7) and the sequence of CGUs in that reach (e.g., its pool–riffle morphology). Therefore, the site for macrohabitat identification is selected by dividing a stream into segments based on geology and local land attributes (Modde et al. 1991), contiguous reaches (e.g., Hankin and Reeves 1988), or reach types (Chapter 7). In turn, the presence, abundance, and sequence of the CGUs help determine the biotic community (Roper and Scarnecchia 1995) and fish life history types likely to be present (Frissell et al. 1986; Bisson and Montgomery 1996). As a result, a stream and its pattern of geomorphic channel units can be placed within the physical context of the stream's entire drainage basin, resulting in a greater understanding of ecological patterns in the stream (Frissell et al. 1986).

No one method for macrohabitat identification has been widely accepted. Many of the methods currently being used are based upon Bisson et al. (1982); however, inconsistent terminology and classification criteria make it difficult to compare studies. Most classification systems are hierarchically organized according to water depth and velocity, bed topography, water surface slope, position relative to the main channel, and features affecting hydrodynamics (e.g., logs, woody debris, boulders; Frissell et al. 1986). Similarities and differences in the combinations of these features allow the CGUs to be grouped in increasingly descriptive categories. Some systems use differences in geomorphic characteristics to differentiate between pools and riffles as primary units, and others prefer to base the classification on slow and fast water types. These base units are general categories under which more specific classes of habitat are organized.

Macrohabitat identification is a useful tool for the inventory and management of stream habitat. It contributes to understanding temporal and spatial changes in habitat within heterogenous stream segments. Macrohabitat identification is used to predict biotic response to changes in habitat availability and suitability, and to identify areas that might support fisheries resources (Bisson et al. 1982; Modde et al. 1991; Hawkins et al. 1993). Fish population estimates can easily be obtained by censusing the different habitats within a stream and sampling a subset of each habitat class for associated fishes (Hawkins et al. 1993). By examining fish responses to manipulations in the abundance and types of CGUs, restoration, enhancement, and fisheries management projects can be designed and evaluated (Hawkins et al. 1993; Flosi and Reynolds 1994). Monitoring projects can more accurately identify stream habitat changes over time that result from enhancement project alterations, management changes, and the cumulative impacts of land-use activities (Frissell et al. 1986; Hankin and Reeves 1988; Hawkins et al. 1993). By comparing stream segments that have similar CGU patterns, site-specific phenomenon (e.g., habitat improvement structures, stream bank failures) can be identified and streams in different drainages can be compared (Bisson and Montgomery 1996).

There are limitations to macrohabitat identification. Most macrohabitat identification methods currently in use are conducted in wadeable streams during base or late summer low flow. They are designed for natural, nonintermittent streams and channels free of human alteration (e.g., dredging, snag clearing). For large streams, the gradual transition between CGUs can make it difficult to distinguish changes. Field identifications can be influenced by observer experience, subjectivity, and inconsistency (Roper and Scarnecchia 1995; Bisson and Montgomery 1996). These points should be seriously considered; however, if standardized techniques and classification systems are adopted, field biologists are properly trained, and the selected techniques are appropriate for the objectives of the assessment (Bisson et al. 1982; Hawkins et al. 1993), macrohabitat identification is a reliable inventory and management tool.

8.1.2 Selection of Techniques

Macrohabitat identification has two components: (1) techniques for the delineation of a stream segment into distinct channel units, and (2) systems for the classification of these units into habitat types. Select a specific delineation technique and classification system before beginning an assessment. The two delineation techniques described in this chapter (channel feature and dimension technique, bed form differencing technique) differ in the way the CGUs are delineated, the number of measurements that need to be taken, and the degree of subjectivity. The three habitat classification systems presented are representative of systems currently in use. These systems may be used singly, in part, or as a combination of parts. Each is hierarchical and has a structure capable of maximum resolution to either three or four levels of complexity. They each distinguish and organize habitat classes differently and use different terminology. However, terminology has been standardized as much as possible, and selected terms are defined in the sections below and in the supporting material.

The channel feature and dimension technique for CGU delineation is compatible with the design of most classification systems, and experienced field staff can rapidly estimate or measure units. It uses systematic sampling and stream habitat sequence observations. The technique is convenient, fast, and relatively easy. The alternative CGU delineation technique, bed form differencing, is reproducible, spatially consistent, and also easy to apply. It is based on a single criterion, accumulated elevation change between bed forms, which is conceptually simple and intuitive (O'Neill and Abrahams 1987). Pools and riffles are delineated on the basis of streambed topography.

Three classification systems are presented: Hawkins system (Hawkins et al. 1993), Flosi and Reynolds system (Flosi and Reynolds 1994), and the Alaska Aquatic Resources Information Management System (AARIMS; Armantrout 1996). The Hawkins system is simple because it uses few habitat classes, subclasses, and levels. The Flosi and Reynolds system includes more levels of classification and more habitat classes than the Hawkins system, but it may overclassify habitats for some assessment objectives by offering too many categories. The AARIMS uses similar terminology as the Flosi and Reynolds system, and has almost as many classes. However, the AARIMS is organized in fewer levels and includes some unique regional habitat types. The AARIMS does not follow the CGUs described by Bisson et al. (1982), upon which most other systems are based.

For all three systems, the classification levels are nested and organized by increasing complexity. For example, a CGU classified as a scour pool at level II is further classified as wood, boulder, or bedrock at level III, depending on which object was responsible for its formation. This system is based on description and the terminology used to describe formative features is provided in detail. This should result in more consistent identification of channel units. Note that some habitat classes were changed by the author to avoid redundancy between levels and these changes can lead to inconsistencies with other systems. Finally, select and stay with one set of techniques, document methodology choices, and avoid adjusting or replacing techniques.

8.2 Delineation: Channel Feature and Dimension Technique

8.2.1 Rationale

The channel feature and dimension technique uses a set of channel shape and hydraulic measurements (modified from Bisson et al. 1982) to define channel geomorphic units (CGUs). The delineation of CGUs is based on the concept that distinct CGUs have characteristic gradient, water velocity, turbulence, substrate, and formative features. The boundaries of each CGU are determined using transect-based measurements of physical features periodically along the stream reach. A habitat area must meet two requirements to be considered a distinct CGU: (1) the measurements or presence of the physical characteristics (listed below) of adjacent units must clearly be different; (2) the largest dimensions of the channel unit should be equal to or greater than the average wetted width of the reach for mid-channel units (on a stream thalweg), or equal to half the average wetted width for CGUs defined along a stream margin (Bisson and Montgomery 1996). Therefore, a series of measurements are recorded along a stream reach and these are used to draw boundaries for CGUs covering the assessment area.

8.2.2 Preparation

▶ Field staff should have prior experience or at least 5 days of training in the identification of CGUs according to the criteria to be used in all macrohabitat identification work. If necessary, acquire permission to work on private land.

▶ Acquire the following surveying equipment: three-part telescoping surveyor's rod; level and clinometer; 1-m metric rule, calibrated rod, or pole; telescoping or folding tripod; materials for establishing the benchmark (see Chapter 6); colored plastic flagging and stakes for marking the assessment site and transect locations. Also obtain waders, a bearing compass, fiberglass metric tape and reel, and a notebook or appropriate data sheet.

8.2.3 Procedures

■ Delineation should occur during periods of low flow unless multiple surveys are planned so that higher flows can be included (see Notes below). Cross section transects should be set up systematically along the thalweg (center line of main streamflow) of the channel in a reach that is approximately 35–40 mean stream widths long (Simonson et al. 1994). For streams greater than 5 m wide, space transects every two stream widths apart. For streams 5 m wide or less, transects may be spaced every three stream widths apart. See Chapter 6 for additional guidance on setting up transects. At each transect estimate or measure the habitat features described below.

  • **Wetted width.** By surveying or using a measuring tape along the transect, obtain the distance perpendicular to the midline channel. Include logs, boulders, stumps, or debris surrounded by water; do not include islands wider than 0.3 m (islands are any accumulation of inorganic sediment particles protruding above the water). Record distances to the nearest 0.1 m and sum the widths of all channels in multi-channel reaches. Repeat this procedure on each transect and calculate the arithmetic mean for the entire reach.

  • **Slope.** See Chapter 6 for the procedure to measure slope and obtain one estimate for each transect using adjacent transects as elevation points.

  • **Stream depth.** Using a calibrated rod, measure water depth (water surface to the stream bottom) to the nearest 0.03 m; read the depth on the downstream side of the rod to avoid inaccuracies due to the wave formed by the rod in moving water. Make depth measurements at three locations that are one-quarter, one-half, and three-quarters the distance across the transect. Calculate the average by dividing the total of the three measurements by 4 for trapezoidal channel shapes (to account for zero depths at the stream shore where the water surface meets the bank of channel) or by 3 for rectangular shapes.

  • **Turbulence.** Turbulence is present if there is a hydraulic jump sufficient to entrain air bubbles and create local patches of white water. Note turbulence at three locations that are one-quarter, one-half, and three-quarters the distance across the transect.

- **Water velocity.** Refer to Chapter 14 for procedures to measure velocity and obtain mean water velocity values at three locations that are one-quarter, one-half, and three-quarters the distance across the transect.

- **Dominant substrate.** Refer to Chapter 9 for categories of substrate types and substrate classification techniques. Record the dominant substrate at three locations that are one-quarter, one-half, and three-quarters the distance across the transect.

■ After collecting the data, define distinct CGUs by delineating instream areas so that the physical characteristics of each CGU are clearly different than those of adjacent units. For channel CGUs, the greatest linear dimension should be equal to or greater than the average wetted width computed from field measurements. For channel margin CGUs, the greatest linear dimension should be equal to half the average wetted width.

■ While in the field, sketch the stream segment and map the location of CGUs, significant flow controlling structures, and other habitat features drawn to scale. Record the maximum length and one (typical) or more widths of each CGU. Maximum CGU length should be oriented parallel to the main channel but not necessarily inclusive of the main channel. Length and width (mean or typical width) measurements can be used to approximate the areas of all CGUs for reporting reach summaries. After CGUs are defined, proceed with classifying the units into habitat types.

8.2.4 Notes

The decision to make visual estimates or take accurate measurements of channel and CGU dimensions depends upon how much time is available and how precise the measurements must be. However, document whichever procedure is selected.

If time and personnel permit, take measurements at a variety of flows, since discharge strongly influences the relative abundance of different CGUs (Bisson and Montgomery 1996).

Contour lines based on depth measurements can be drawn within the pools to estimate volume; wetted surface areas can be estimated by counting squares on gridded paper superimposed on the maps (see lake area estimates described in Chapter 16).

8.3 Delineation: Bed Form Differencing Technique

8.3.1 Rationale

O'Neill and Abrahams (1987) developed an objective technique for distinguishing pools and riffles in a stream segment. Streambed elevation changes are used to identify the locations of pool and riffle habitats (Figure 8.1). Undulations in the bed profile are measured and when the elevation change exceeds a segment specific tolerance value, a minimum or maximum elevation is designated. When a minimum or maximum value is followed by an opposing value, the previous minimum or maximum value is identified as a pool or riffle. Absolute minimum values delineate a pool and absolute maximum values delineate riffles. The procedure presented here is for pool–riffle sequences common to naturally formed stream channels, but the technique can be applied to altered streams by modifying the tolerance calculation and sampling interval length.

8.3.2 Preparation

▶ Field staff should have experience conducting elevation and distance surveying as described in Chapter 6 for longitudinal profile measurements. If necessary, acquire permission to work on private land.

▶ Acquire the following surveying equipment: three-part telescoping surveyor's rod, level, telescoping or folding tripod, materials for establishing the benchmark (see Chapter 6), colored plastic flagging and stakes for marking pool and riffle locations. Also obtain waders, fiberglass metric tape and reel, and a notebook or appropriate data sheet.

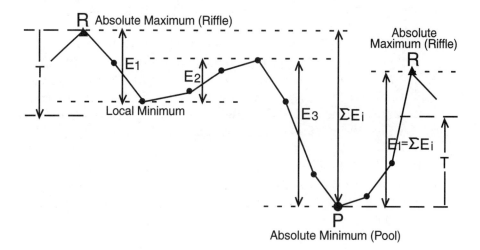

Figure 8.1   Hypothetical bed profile illustrating the approach and terminology for the bed form differencing technique (from O'Neill and Abrahams 1987).

8.3.3 Procedures

■ Bed elevation surveys are most easily done at low flows when the riffle and pool features are easily recognized. Measure bed elevation by differential leveling (see Chapter 6) along the center of the channel at intervals approximately equal to mean channel width (estimate with a series of width measurements along the stream reach). The survey equipment readings will yield the inverse (from level height down) of elevation but subtracting from an arbitrary base level (e.g., 1,000 cm) will produce proper elevation readings. Shorten the measurement intervals if obvious errors occur because riffles and pools are close together. Working downstream, measure a series of increasing bed elevations (B_1, B_2, B_3, …). When the values begin to decrease, use the last high point as the starting location (first maximum or riffle) for data collection.

■ Continue measuring a series of elevations, and perform the calculations as shown in Table 8.1. The values in Table 8.1 correspond to four examples shown graphically in Figure 8.2. Include enough observations in the series so that a distinct change in water surface elevation separating pool and riffle habitat is identified. Calculate the standard deviation (SD) of the resulting difference values ($B_1 - B_2$, $B_2 - B_3$, … [$B_{(i+1)} - B_i$]) as shown in Table 8.1. Set the tolerance value (T) at $0.75 \times$ SD if the sample spacing approximates the average stream width. Note the sign of the change in elevation with subsequent measurements. A series (E) of elevation changes is a set of consecutive difference values with the same sign. Number the series ($E_{1, 2, 3, …}$) as in Table 8.1. Calculate the total elevation change for the series (ΣE_i) by summing the bed elevation differences. Compare the total elevation changes for each series against the tolerance value (T), and note those that are equal or larger than T. Mark these minimum or maximum points along the stream margin with flagging or a visible stake. If the next downstream minimum or maximum point is the same type (either lower or higher than the preceding), then the preceding point is a local minimum or maximum and of no further significance. When a minimum or maximum is followed by an opposing point that exceeds or equals T, a riffle or pool location is designated (Table 8.1, Figure 8.2). Leave markers for these points and remove the others.

■ After pools and riffles are identified for a reach, classify the units into habitat types. Not all terms will be relevant, but subcategories of the pool and riffle habitats are provided for further characterization.

Table 8.1 Example calculations of the bed form differencing technique for identifying riffles and pools in streams. Cases correspond to plots in Figure 8.2 and the sample field measurements are the bed elevations (B_i) in arbitrary units such as centimeters from a given base mark.

Oberva-tion (i)	B (ith)	$B_{(i+1)} - B_i$	Sign of change	Series (i)	Series ΣE_i	$\lvert\Sigma E_i\rvert \geq T$?	Designation
				Example A			
1	39						Start or upstream bed form
2	29	−10	−	1			
3	9	−20	−	1			
4	6	− 3	−	1	−33	Yes	Absolute minimum; pool
5	12	6	+	2			
6	24	12	+	2			
7	35	11	+	2	29	Yes	Absolute maximum; riffle
	SD = 12.7			Net change = − 4			
	T = 9.5						
				Example B			
1	46						Start or upstream bed form
2	37	− 9	−	1			
3	26	−11	−	1	−20	Yes	Local minimum
4	29	3	+	2	3	No	Less than T, not a bed form
5	19	−10	−	3	−10	Yes	Absolute minimum; pool
6	20	1	+	4			
7	24	4	+	4			
8	30	6	+	4			
9	42	12	+	4	23	Yes	Absolute maximum; riffle
	SD = 8.5			Net change = − 4			
	T = 6.4						
				Example C			
1	45						Start or upstream bed form
2	31	−14	−	1	−14	Yes	Local minimium
3	37	6	+	2	6	No	Less than T, not a bed form
4	35	− 2	−	3	− 2	No	Less than T, not a bed form
5	36	1	+	4	1	No	Less than T, not a bed form
6	21	−15	−	5			
7	14	− 7	−	5	−22	Yes	Absolute minimum; pool
8	30	16	+	6			
9	42	12	+	6	28	Yes	Absolute maximum; riffle
	SD = 11.4			Net change = − 3			
	T = 8.6						
				Example D			
1	43						Start or upstream bed form
2	32	−11	−	1			
3	22	−10	−	1	−21	Yes	Local minimium
4	25	3	+	2	3	No	Less than T, not a bed form
5	18	− 7	−	3	− 7	No	Less than T, not a bed form
6	22	4	+	4	4	No	Less than T, not a bed form
7	7	−15	−	5	−15	Yes	Absolute minimum; pool
8	12	5	+	6			
9	38	26	+	6	31	Yes	Absolute maximum; riffle
	SD = 13.2			Net change = − 5			
	T = 9.9						

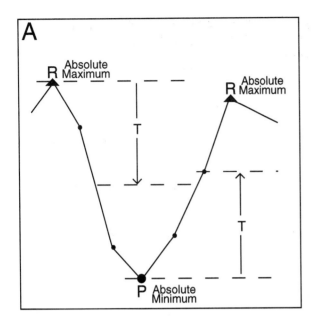

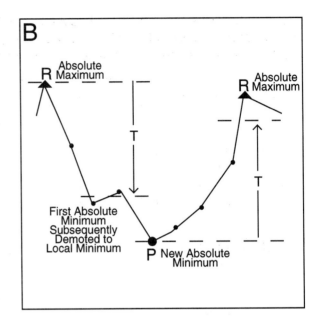

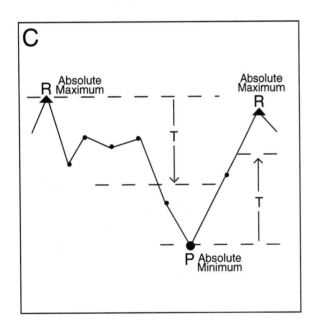

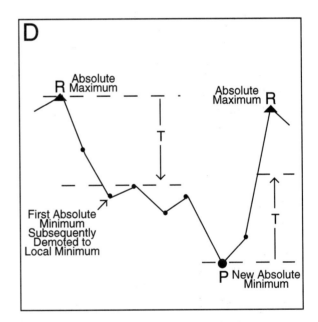

Figure 8.2 Example bed profiles showing the bed form differencing technique. Charts A, B, C, and D correspond with sample calculations in Table 8.1 (modified from O'Neill and Abrahams 1987).

8.3.4 Notes

With some field experience, it will not be necessary to use or retain a data sheet because the technique is easy to follow and key values will identify pools and riffles.

8.4 Macrohabitat Classification

8.4.1 Rationale

Three similar macrohabitat classification systems are provided in this section, and any one or a combination of systems can be used to classify CGUs or riffles and pools identified by the delineation techniques presented above. Select a classification system based on assessment objectives, desired level of detail, and regional usability. Habitat descriptors for fast water or riffles (Table 8.2) and slow water or pools (Table 8.3) are provided with illustrations (Figures 8.3 and 8.4) to guide the identification of habitat classes.

Hawkins et al. (1993) describe a three-level system that can be used to classify CGUs for riffle (fast water) and pool (slow water) habitat classes (Figure 8.5). Fast water habitats are subdivided based on differences in gradient, bed roughness, and step development (distinct breaks in bed slope) that result in turbulent or nonturbulent flow. Pool classes are distinguished according to location within the flood or active channel, longitudinal and cross-sectional depth profiles, substrate characteristics, and constraining features that impound water. Flosi and Reynolds (1994) developed a four-level classification system (Figure 8.6) where the first two levels are similar to the first two levels of the Hawkins system. The more detailed levels of the Flosi and Reynolds system are based on water surface gradient for riffles and stream channel structures and location for pools. At level IV, a wide range of habitat classes are provided making this the most detailed of the three systems. Finally, the AARIMS system (Alaska Aquatic Resources Information Management System; Armantrout 1996) has nearly as many habitat classes as the Flosi and Reynolds system but in three levels (Figure 8.7). Complex habitat classes are included at the second level of resolution, which makes the AARIMS system unique. A complex habitat is a combination of fast water, slow water, and standing water habitats, which are too small to be split apart well in most CGU delineations.

8.4.2 Preparation

▶ Before field observations, delineate the study reach into CGUs or riffles and pools for classifying habitat types.

▶ Determine which classification system and level of resolution will be used for habitat classifications.

Table 8.2   Fast water macrohabitats and their characteristics.

Habitat type	Turbulence	Velocity	Substrate	Slope	Stream reach type	Miscellaneous
Low gradient or riffle	moderate; little– no whitewater; high at points of channel constriction	moderate: 20–50 cm/s	gravel, pebble, cobble; totally–partially submerged	<4%	plane bed, pool–riffle, regime, braided	channel profile usually straight to convex
High gradient or rapid	considerable; whitewater	fast; >50 cm/s	cobble, boulder; course, exposed	4–7%	plane bed	steps and pocket pools common; planar longitudinal profile
Steep gradient or cascade	high; mainly whitewater	high	bedrock or accumulation of boulders	>7%	bedrock, cascade	series of small falls or steps and pools; stepped longitudinal profile
Falls	high; whitewater	free falling over vertical drop		≤100%	bedrock, cascade, step pool	formed from a full spanning flow obstruction
Steps		fast		10–100%		abrupt breaks in gradient; usually shorter than channel width; features include: bedrock, boulders, cobble bar, logs, culvert, dam, weir
Chutes	turbulent	swift	bedrock; little– none exposed	2–30%	bedrock, cascade, step pool	can be in narrow, steep slots in bedrock
Glides	nonturbulent	low–moderate; even	gravel, cobble, sand	0–1%		wide channel lacking a definite thalweg; usually at the transition between a pool and riffle; no major flow ob- structions; lacks features associated with pools; moderately shallow (10–30 cm)
Run	nonturbulent	swift	gravel, cobble, boulder	low	pool–riffle, regime, braided	occurs over a definite thalweg flat plane with a uniform channel form; no major flow obstructions; moderately shallow; deeper than riffles
Sheets	nonturbulent	uniform	smooth bedrock	variable	bedrock, cascade, step pool	
Edgewater	nonturbulent	low–still	varies from cobbles to boulders			usually associated with riffles; along margins of stream

Table 8.3 Slow water macrohabitats and their characteristics.

Habitat type	Substrate	Formation	Features	Stream reach type	Miscellaneous
Pool		lateral constriction of channel or sharp drop in water surface profile	bend in channel, large-scale obstructions (e.g., boulder, log)		concave in shape; direction of flow varies widely; depth greater than riffles or runs
Straight scour	highly variable	mid-channel scour caused by flow constriction	laterally confined, hardened banks; boulders or woody debris obstructions	cascade, step pool, pool–riffle	hole encompasses >60% of wetted channel width; symmetrical cross section; deeper at head
Lateral scour	variable	partial channel obstruction constricts flow to one side of channel	undercut bank, channel bend, log, root wad, bedrock outcrop, boulder	step pool, pool–riffle, regime, braided	scour usually confined to <60% of wetted channel width; deepest along bank with obstruction
Backwater eddy	fine-grained (sand, gravel, cobble)	eddy scour downstream of a large obstruction along channel margin	root wad, boulder, log	almost all reach types	deep; >30 cm
Trench	stable; mainly bedrock	scour due to tightly constrained channel	bedrock walls are highly resistant to erosion	bedrock-dominated	U-shaped cross section; very long and narrow; swift velocity; deep; uniform
Channel confluence		scour occurring at confluence of two or more channels	partical sorting, plunges, lateral obstructions	any type of reach	also called convergence; greater velocity and turbulence than most other pool types
Plunge	partical size highly variable	scour due to water falling vertically over a complete or nearly complete channel obstruction	logs, boulder, bedrock	small, steep headwater streams; bedrock, cascade, step pool	deep; >1 m
Step	boulder			high-gradient, mountain streams	pools separated by short riffles or cascades
Dammed	smaller gravels and sand	water impounded upstream due to a complete or nearly complete channel blockage	debris jam, beaver, landslide		temporary nature because fill up with sediments (rate depends on sediment source)
Secondary isolated	gravel, sand, silt	outside of wetted but within active channel; water prevented from entering secondary channel	gravel bars; any other feature preventing flow from main to secondary channel	pool–riffle, regime, braided	after freshets; may dry up or depend on intergravel flow during late summer
Alcove pocket water	typically sand and organic matter, but can be of any type	outside active channel, into a secondary channel or along margins; eddy scour near lateral obstruction	boulders, rubble, logs		length usually less than full channel width; low–still velocity
Abandoned channel		formed at low flow when bars deposited along main channel isolate water in secondary channels		pool–riffle, regime, braided	ephemeral or maintained by subsurface flow

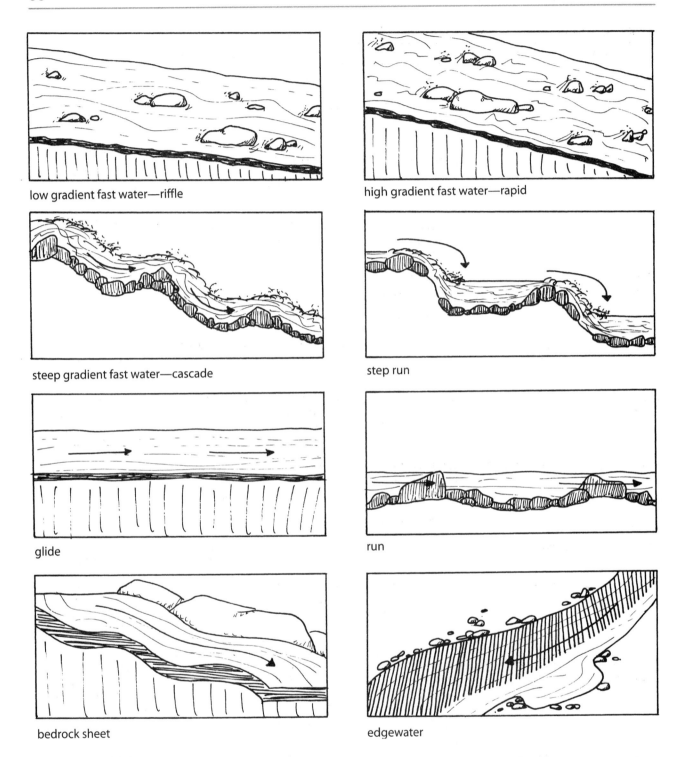

low gradient fast water—riffle

high gradient fast water—rapid

steep gradient fast water—cascade

step run

glide

run

bedrock sheet

edgewater

Figure 8.3   Illustrations of fast water habitat classes (from Flosi and Reynolds 1994).

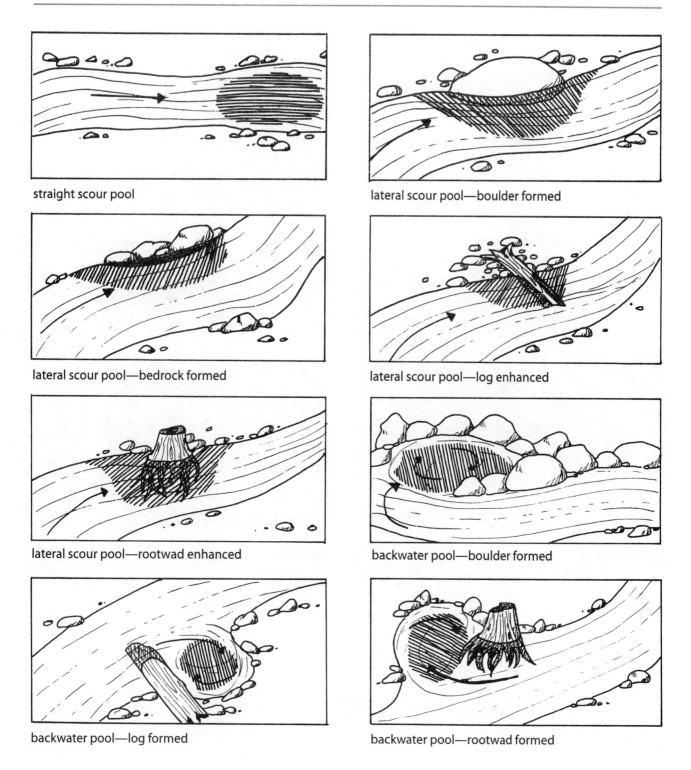

straight scour pool

lateral scour pool—boulder formed

lateral scour pool—bedrock formed

lateral scour pool—log enhanced

lateral scour pool—rootwad enhanced

backwater pool—boulder formed

backwater pool—log formed

backwater pool—rootwad formed

Figure 8.4   Illustrations of slow water habitat classes (from Flosi and Reynolds 1994).

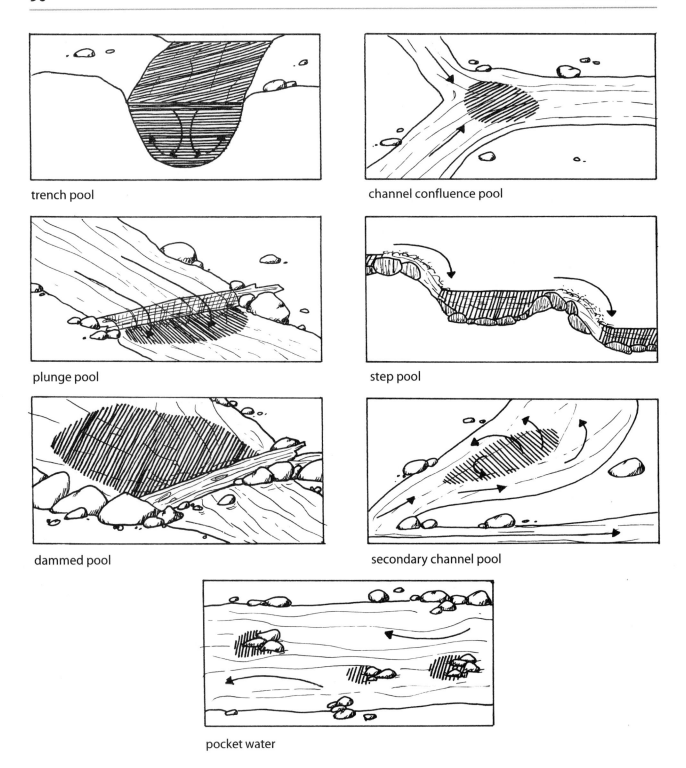

trench pool

channel confluence pool

plunge pool

step pool

dammed pool

secondary channel pool

pocket water

Figure 8.4   Illustrations of slow water habitat classes, *continued* (from Flosi and Reynolds 1994).

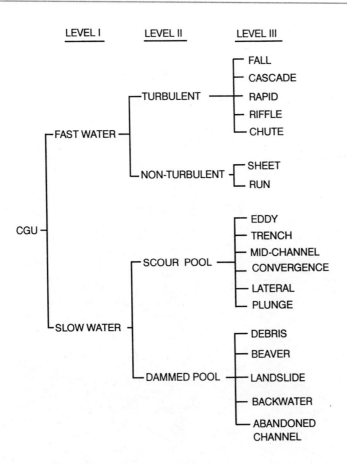

Figure 8.5   Dendrogram of the Hawkins habitat classification system (from Hawkins et al. 1993).

▶ Have the appropriate habitat type descriptions (Tables 8.2 and 8.3) and example illustrations (Figures 8.3 and 8.4) ready for use in the field. Prepare a check-off form that identifies the previously delineated habitats.

8.4.3 Procedure

▪ Classify each habitat by observation and measurements (e.g., maximum velocity, slope) as needed using Tables 8.2 and 8.3 and the sample habitat class illustrations (Figures 8.3 and 8.4) as guides. Record habitat types so that they correspond with information recorded in the delineation tasks. Label habitats on a sketch or scale map of the assessment reach.

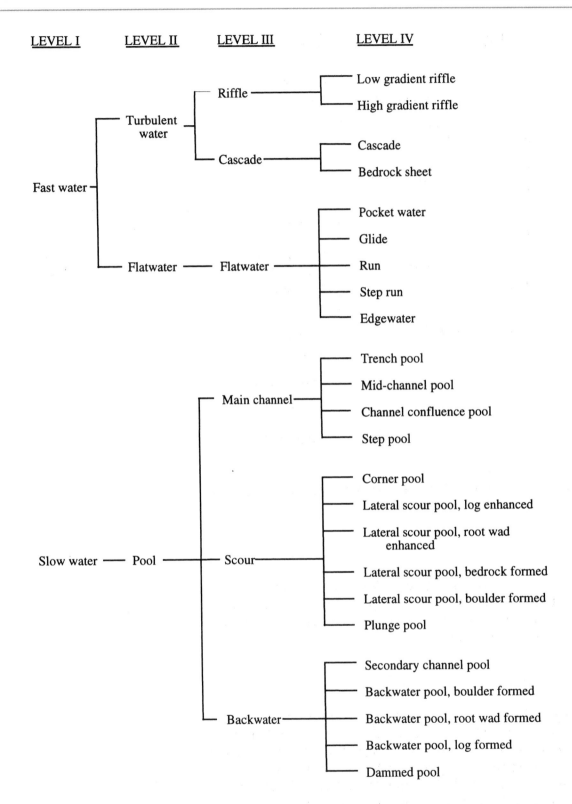

Figure 8.6   Dendrogram of the Flosi and Reynolds habitat classification system (modified from Flosi and Reynolds 1994).

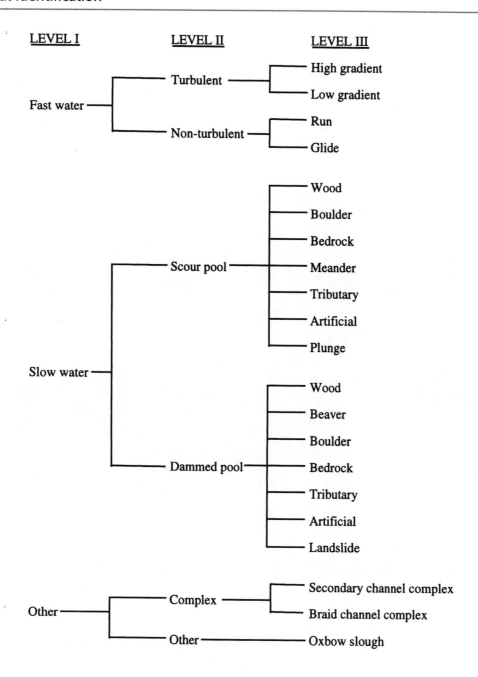

Figure 8.7   Dendrogram of the AARIMS habitat classification system (adapted from Armantrout 1996).

8.4.4 Notes

Not all of Flosi and Reynold's habitat classes are represented in the descriptive tables and illustrations because combinations of attributes are sometimes used to define a particular class and some consolidation of information was done for consistency across classification methods.

A fourth level of detail was included in the original AARIMS system (Armantrout 1996) but is not presented here because it was judged to be too detailed for broad use.

Substrate

9

Mark B. Bain

9.1 Introduction

9.1.1 Background

Substrate refers to the bottom material of a water body, and it is almost always documented in habitat surveys. There are three reasons for measuring substrate in any type of habitat assessment.

1. The composition of the substrate determines the roughness of stream channels, and roughness has a large influence on channel hydraulics (water depth, width, and current velocity) of stream habitat.
2. Substrate provides the micro-conditions needed by many fish species. For example, many species require specific substrates for spawning because eggs adhere to some surfaces. Also the interstitial water flow through the substrate maintains high oxygen levels around buried eggs (e.g., salmonids, see Chapman 1988).
3. Substrate provides clues to local and watershed influences on stream habitat quality. Land surface disturbances caused by forestry and agricultural practices alter surface water runoff and sedimentation rates, and these processes are reflected in the size composition of surface substrate (Meehan 1991).

As one of the most important aspects of fish habitat, substrate has often been measured or characterized using many techniques.

9.1.2 Selection of Techniques

A field technique is described that is especially relevant to each of the three functions associated with substrate. A rapid field technique (frequency of size classes) is described in section 9.2 to document simple substrate composition in a way that allows the data to be used in a variety of reports and further analyses. Although simplistic, substrate size-class composition will provide a means for consistently characterizing the general nature of stream substrate. A field technique is described in section 9.3 (embeddedness) for measuring the extent that interstitial spaces between coarse substrate particles are filled with fine material. This technique is especially relevant when habitat assessments target fish spawning habitat quality for species that bury eggs; notably salmonids. Finally, a technique is presented in section 9.4 (pebble count) that quantifies substrate size composition in a way that can be easily related to land use influences. This technique is commonly used when habitat assessments are oriented to watershed-scale conditions. The three techniques are ordered from the easiest and fastest to the most involved and informative. The pebble count method provides information that encompasses the other techniques, and when it is used all information commonly sought in substrate assessments is obtained.

9.2   Assessment of Composition: Frequency of Size Classes

9.2.1 Rationale

The goal of substrate assessments is to describe the dominant type or types of bottom material. Assessments are often done visually; for example, reporting that the littoral zone of a lake is largely sand. With little additional effort, a series of repeated observations can be used to develop a more quantitative assessment of substrate composition. The basic approach is to make a series of categorical observations of dominant substrate, and then treat those observations as data for statistical description. Statistical description of a series of substrate observations identifies the dominant material and the variability in the mixture of material that makes up the substrate.

It is necessary to categorize substrate types for making visual designations in the field. Substrate types have long been organized on a geometric size scale (the Wentworth scale, Wentworth 1922), in which each size category is twice as big as the preceding one. The Wentworth scale was grouped into familiar substrate types (e.g., sand, gravel, pebble) by Cummins (1962) and this modified Wentworth classification (Table 9.1) is frequently used in fish habitat studies because categories are easily distinguished for field surveys. Bain et al. (1985) described how the modified Wentworth classification can be used in a series of substrate observations to describe mean substrate size and substrate heterogeneity. This technique can also be used to directly measure the dominant substrate.

Table 9.1   Modified Wentworth classification of substrate types by size (Cummins 1962).

Substrate type	Particle size range (mm)	Sample codes
Boulder	>256	5
Cobble	64–256	4
Pebble	16–63	3
Gravel	2–15	2
Sand	0.06–1	1
Silt and clay	<0.059	0

9.2.2 Preparation

▶ Acquire one or more lead-core ropes or chains (1-m to 2-m lengths depending on habitat size) with 10-cm sections painted contrasting colors.

▶ Prior to fieldwork, develop a plan that specifies the number of observations to be made at a location, and the number of locations spaced across a study site. For example, in large streams a 2-m rope can be used to make 20 observations at a stream location, and 10 of these sample sets would yield a total of 200 observations.

9.2.3 Procedures

■ **Make a series of substrate observations.** At each sampling location on the bottom of a stream or lake littoral zone, record the dominant substrate class in contact with each colored section of rope. The dominant substrate class will often vary by colored section, and dominant substrates can be rapidly judged for each section. Record the substrate types using the class codes in Table 9.1 and as shown in the sample data in Table 9.2. Repeat this procedure at predetermined intervals across the study site. The first location should be randomly selected and the others should follow at set intervals (e.g., every third meter across representative transects). In small streams, use a 1-m sampling rope to obtain 10 observations, and use the rope at least 10 times for a total of 100 observations. For large water bodies, a 2-m rope with 20 colored segments can be used; at least 10 samplings with the rope should be made across a study site.

■ **Characterize the substrate for the study site.** Compute the mean of all substrate observations (e.g., $N = 100$ or 200) to estimate the average substrate size, the dominant substrate for the entire site, and the standard deviation to indicate substrate heterogeneity. Example statistics and their interpretations are given in Table 9.2 for single rope samples; a much larger series of numbers would be obtained and analyzed for a whole study site. The computations and interpretations would be the same but based on more observations.

Table 9.2   Sample coded substrate data from four sets of observations in different habitats with descriptive statistics and inferred substrate composition (from Bain et al. 1985). Actual field data for a study site would include 100 or 200 observations for each study site but the statistics and interpretations would be the same.

Substrate observations	Dominant (mode)	Mean	Standard deviation	Inferred substrate composition
5555511112111145555	Boulder	3.20	±1.96	Heterogeneous mix of sand and boulders
5555555555555555555	Boulder	5.00	±0.00	Homogeneous boulder
1111222111111122111	Sand	1.25	±0.44	Nearly homogeneous, fine
2223344432544443333	Pebble	3.25	±0.85	Intermediate mixture

9.2.4 Notes

This technique is simple, straightforward, and rapid to conduct. With some field experience, one person could quickly call out substrate codes and an assistant could record the observations. A set of observations can be completed in a minute or two after the rope is positioned on the substrate. Data derived from this technique should complement data on water depth, velocity, and other continuous habitat attributes. Although this is a rapid field technique, the level of resolution is sufficient to meet most management needs. Several numerical descriptive measures (subdominant substrates, range of types, and class frequencies) can be generated with the data collected in addition to those recommended above and in Table 9.2. The technique can be applied to lakes although it may be necessary to modify the gear (sampling rope or chain).

9.3   Assessment of Structure: Embeddedness

9.3.1 Rationale

Embeddedness is a substrate attribute reflecting the degree to which larger particles (boulder, cobble, pebble, and large gravel) are surrounded or covered by fine sediment such as sand, silt, or clay. Fine sediment can fill the interstitial spaces between large particles and block water flow important for quality substrate habitat to support benthic macroinvertebrates, small overwintering fish, some fish spawning, and egg incubation. Substrates with heavy interstitial filling are described as highly embedded and degraded in benthic habitat quality.

9.3.2 Preparation

▶ Conduct embeddedness assessment after substrate sizes have been described in qualitative or quantitative (section 9.2) terms. Observers should have experience in distinguishing between, gravel, cobble, and boulders. A reference sample (bag, large jar, or box) of particles in the size range for each substrate class (Table 9.1) is very helpful for training field staff to classify substrates by sight.

9.3.3 Procedures

■ **Record a series of field observations.** Using the criteria in Table 9.3, classify the embeddedness of the channel in five or more representative habitats (riffle, run, pool) on the thalweg or midstream locations. If the site is being assessed with transects, embeddedness can be recorded for midstream or thalweg locations on each transect. Report the modal (most common) rating for the site.

9.3.4 Notes

This technique is simple to conduct although the visual assessment of embeddedness is not highly accurate. Therefore, this technique is intended to approximate the condition of substrate relative to fine sediment impacts, and this is often sufficient to meet many management evaluation needs. It is not known what level of embeddedness is optimal for many fish species, and consequently coarse assessments should be satisfactory. The technique cannot be applied to lakes since interstitial space and water flow are based on flowing water bed dynamics.

Table 9.3   Embeddedness rating for stream channel materials (from Platts et al. 1983). Fine sediment includes material less than 2 mm in diameter: sand, silt, and clay.

Level of embeddedness	Description
Negligible	Gravel, pebble, cobble, and boulder particles have <5% of their surface covered by fine sediment
Low	Gravel, pebble, cobble, and boulder particles have 5–25% of their surface covered by fine sediment
Moderate	Gravel, pebble, cobble, and boulder particles have 25–50% of their surface covered by fine sediment
High	Gravel, cobble, and boulder particles have 50–75% of their surface covered by fine sediment
Very high	Gravel, pebble, cobble, and boulder particles have >75% of their surface covered by fine sediment

9.4 Assessment of Size–Frequency Distribution: Pebble Counts

9.4.1 Rationale

Fisheries biologists have relied heavily on visual characterizations of substrate composition using the techniques described above. An alternative practical and rapid technique yields substrate measurements, which enhances the repeatability and comparability of substrate assessments. The Wolman pebble count procedure (Wolman 1954) has been modified (Potyondy and Hardy 1994) to produce this technique which is especially suited for relating land activities to stream habitat quality (Figure 9.1). To use this technique, the investigator records the measurement of a single dimension for each substrate particle and repeats this measurement for a series of particles collected at the stream site. Evaluation of pebble counts has supported its use as a rapid method for quantitative analyses superior in accuracy and assessment performance to visual characterizations (Kondolf and Li 1992; Bevenger and King 1995). The technique also yields particle size data that can be used to compute frequency distributions, summary statistics, and parameters used in hydraulic analyses.

9.4.2 Preparation

▶ Obtain a hand ruler, caliper, and data sheet as shown in Figure 9.2.

▶ Inspect study site to obtain approximate stream width and site length.

9.4.3 Procedure

■ **Design a sampling plan.** At the stream study site, set up about 12 zig-zag transects (see Figure 9.2) with bank intersection points spaced apart at a distance approximately twice the typical stream width (just visually estimate this spacing). Roughly estimate a distance interval to use on all transects (e.g., every second foot of length) to get about ten sampling points per transect. The total number of substrate observations should be 100, but there are no disadvantages to recording more observations. Twelve transects should ensure enough samples to account for variation in transect lengths.

■ **Collect pebble measurements.** Proceed along all transects at a predetermined interval, pick a particle at toepoint, and measure the intermediate axis (see Figure 9.3 for a description) in millimeters (mm) using a ruler or caliper. The technique is illustrated in Figure 9.2 from Bevenger and King (1995). If boulders are too large to pick up, take an approximate measurement in the field by holding a ruler above the boulder assuming the two largest

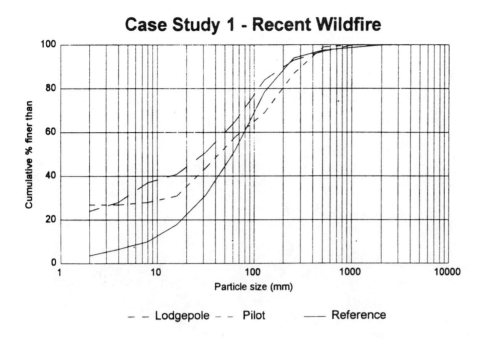

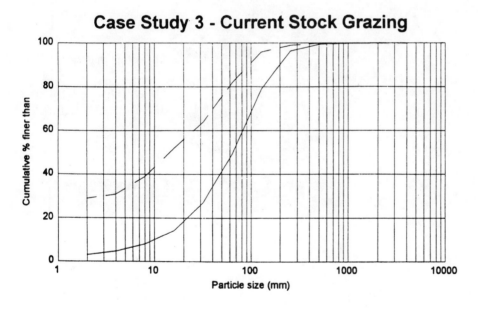

Figure 9.1   Particle size distributions from the pebble count technique for case study streams and reference sites (from Bevenger and King 1995).

dimensions are visible. For any particle under 2 mm on the intermediate axis, record the size as less than 2 mm. Include all channel areas on the transect that appear to be covered by water sometime during the year.

■ **Prepare results.** Sort data points into rank order and plot every 10th percentile point as in Figure 9.1 to plot a cumulative frequency line. Percentile points on the plot correspond with vari-

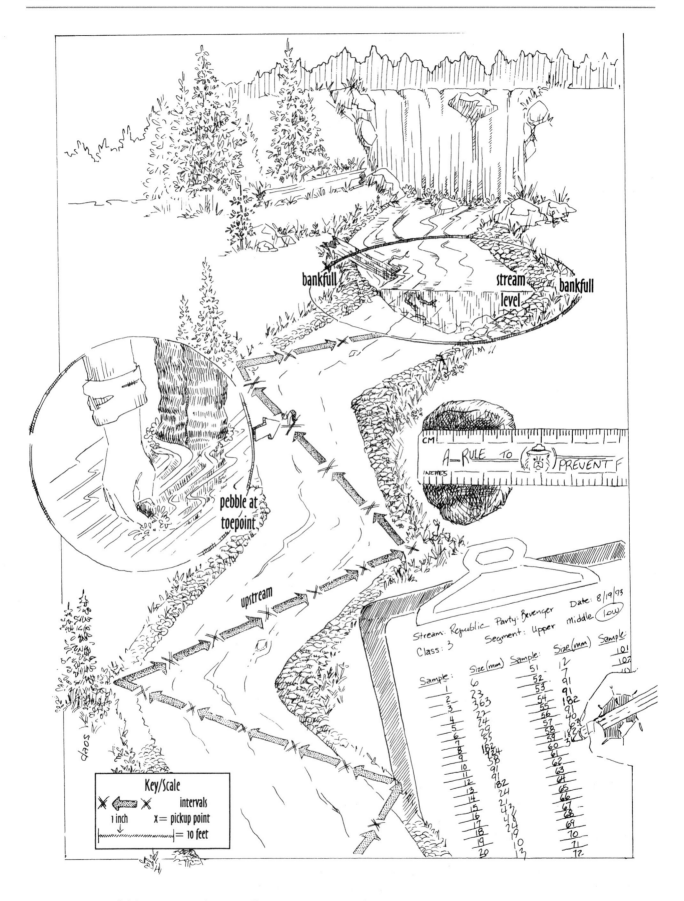

Figure 9.2   Pebble count technique (from Bevenger and King 1995).

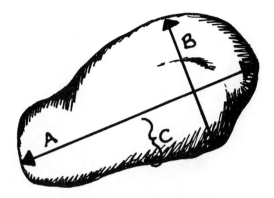

A = longest axis (length)
B = intermediate axis (width)
C = shortest axis (thickness)

Figure 9.3   The intermediate axis of a particle, defined as neither the longest nor the shortest of mutually perpendicular axes, is measured to the nearest millimeter. The intermediate axis can be visualized as the dimension of the particle that controls whether or not it could pass through a sieve (from Harrelson et al. 1994).

ous measures (e.g., middle 50% size range, median, range, etc.) including the size of median (50th percentile) diameter used in many hydraulic formulae.

9.4.4 Notes

The accuracy of the pebble count technique depends on unbiased selection of particles, and that can be difficult to achieve consistently in some field situations. However, a clear sampling plan and careful particle selection often yields data that detect minor substrate composition differences among similar sites. This technique has been evaluated and used in the western mountain region of the United States; no information is available on its application in other regions. The technique cannot be applied to lakes since inference is based on flowing water sediment dynamics. The value of the data distribution for inference can be limited in naturally fine sediment coastal sand bed streams.

Cover and Refuge

10

Nathalie J. Stevenson and Mark B. Bain

10.1 Introduction

10.1.1 Background

Biologists consider the availability of cover in both lakes and streams to be important for maintaining many species and life stages of fish. Cover provides refuge (e.g., Tabor and Wurtsbaugh 1991) for fish from aquatic, terrestrial, and airborne (bird) predators as well as physical conditions such as high current velocities and bright sunlight. Organisms on which fish feed attach themselves to cover. Cover includes boulders and logs, aquatic vegetation, water turbulence, and concealing water depths (Armantrout 1998). While cover heavily influences the species, size, and life stage of fish found in a stream or lake habitat, cover and fish community relations are often complex. We present different techniques for documenting cover and refuge, and techniques for measuring the extent of cover.

10.1.2 Selection of Techniques

Many methods to assess cover have been developed, but they differ regarding what constitutes cover and how to best measure it. The techniques described here differ in fundamental ways as well. Section 10.2 presents techniques for measuring cover composition and abundance defined by single habitat attributes that provide cover and refuge for fish: deep water, turbulence, wood debris, and aquatic vegetation. The single-factor techniques are useful when one type of cover is of primary interest, for example, macrophyte beds in the littoral zone of lakes, or when one type of cover is the only one present, such as turbulence in fast-flowing, high montane streams. These techniques are also useful if habitat assessment is driven by the need to enhance or preserve one particular species of fish that depends on one or a few types of cover. Finally, the single-factor techniques can be used in concert with the more comprehensive cover assessment techniques described later. The result is a method that mixes general cover quantification with information on some specific cover features.

The techniques presented in sections 10.3 (Structural Complexity) and 10.4 (Cover Density) are used to evaluate cover indirectly by measuring physical structure features that are the consequence of cover. The technique used to assess structural complexity requires measuring topographic variability that is caused by cover objects. The technique used to assess cover density requires counting the number of objects that intersect a plane that extends between the water surface and the substrate. However, neither of these techniques identify the composition of cover in any assessed habitat. For a thorough assessment of cover, a combination of some or all of the techniques in section 10.2 could be used to document both the types and spatial extent of cover in a habitat.

10.2 Cover Composition and Abundance

10.2.1 Rationale

Stream morphology and water depth are positively correlated with abundance of certain fish species (Jowett et al. 1996) and life stages (Johnson et al. 1992; Aadland 1993; Carpenter and Maughan 1993). Depending on the water transparency, water depth provides surface concealment, and the availability of such water depth is considered as cover here. The techniques for measuring stream width and depth are covered in Chapter 6, and techniques for measuring transparency are covered in Chapter 17.

Turbulence is when water movement disturbs the surface and reduces the visibility of objects in water (Armantrout 1998). Turbulence is often important where little or no structural cover is present, but it is difficult to quantify the degree of turbulence needed to provide cover and refuge for particular species or sizes of fish. Consequently, we provide a simple but approximate technique for estimating the extent of turbulence. Large wood debris provides cover and usually improves both the quality and quantity of fish habitat (Lisle 1986; Everett and Ruiz 1993). Wood debris retards current velocity, adds structure, and increases the volume of usable habitat for some fish in small streams during periods of low flow (Lisle 1986). We include a technique for measuring the amount of wood debris in samples of habitat.

Many fish species are attracted to vegetation and rely on plant cover during some stage of their life. Studies that compare fish abundance in vegetated and unvegetated habitats have shown that abundance is usually much higher in vegetated areas for sunfish *Lepomis* spp., bass *Micropterus* spp., and northern pike *Esox lucius*. However, pelagic species, such as white bass *Morone chrysops*, gizzard shad

Dorosoma cepedianum, and inland silverside *Menidia beryllina*, are less abundant in highly vegetated habitats (Dibble et al. 1996). Very high vegetation density may cause decreased foraging efficiency for some important fishes. Some fish species are obligate plant spawners: at least 12 freshwater fish families use aquatic vegetation as nursery habitat for larvae, and at least 19 families of freshwater fish occupy vegetated habitats during at least one of their life stages (Dibble et al. 1996). Quantified relations between optimal fish species composition, biomass, density, and cover of aquatic vegetation are very limited despite many studies. However, intermediate (10–40% areal coverage) plant densities enhance fish diversity, feeding, growth, and reproduction (Dibble et al. 1996). The following technique yields broad measures of cover from structured visual estimation, since highly quantitative methods are not yet available for predicting habitat quality.

10.2.2 Preparation

▶ Measure and record representative stream widths and the maximum water depths that allow the substrate to be seen.

▶ Assemble waterproof measuring tapes, meter sticks, stakes and flagging for temporary transect marking, a field guide to common aquatic plants, and a small boat for deep water.

10.2.3 Procedures

■ **Arrange transects and sections.** In shallow streams where most or all of the substrate is visible, set up 12 zig-zag transects with bank intersection points spaced apart by a distance approximately twice the typical stream width (visually estimate spacing). Create five or six sections per transect by roughly estimating a distance interval to use on all transects (e.g., every 2 m). There should be about 50 transect sections, but there are no disadvantages to including more. This zig-zag transect design is the same one recommended for substrate measurements in Chapter 9 and illustrated in Figure 9.2. To add cover observations, form five sections by making each section span the distance between every other substrate measurement point (about 10 per transect). For large streams and rivers, design transects in a similar way but do not sample the sections where the water is regularly so deep that the substrate is not visible from above. Record the sections where deep water provides cover as shown on the data sheet in Figure 10.1. In lakes and reservoirs, place transects perpendicular to the shoreline extending to the outer edge of the littoral zone. Subsection lengths and the number of transects should evenly cover the area of interest.

■ **Estimate extent of turbulence in streams.** Visually estimate the percentage of the linear distance within each full transect section where the surface is broken. Turbulence is indicated by presence of spray, bubbles, white water, evident depressions, and elevations in the surface. For each full section, record (example in Figure 10.1) whether the water surface has negligible turbulence (<5% broken water surface), little turbulence (5–10% broken water surface), minor turbulence (11–40%), substantial turbulence (41–75%), or extensive turbulence (>75% broken water surface). Sum the number of sections and the distances counted in each turbulence class.

■ **Enumerate wood debris.** For each full transect section, count and measure the diameter (to the nearest centimeter at the transect line) of all pieces of woody debris greater than one centimeter in diameter that intercept the transect line. Tally and record the number of wood pieces by diameter class (1–5, 6–10, 11–50, >51 cm) for each section (example in Figure 10.1). Sum the number of pieces in each size-class for all transect sections. Calculate the length of all transect sections and calculate the average number of pieces per section or linear length of transect.

■ **Estimate extent of vegetation cover.** For each full transect section, estimate the approximate linear length with significant vegetation and record the dominant vegitation type: emergent, floating, or submerged (see Figure 10.1). Sum the linear distance (percents of section length) on all surveyed transect sections by vegetation class including no vegetation. Very common and dominant taxa should be noted.

10.2.4 Notes

This technique is based on general classes of cover (i.e., deep water, minor turbulence, abundant wood debris). Habitat assessments conducted in this way should result in data that can be used to estimate cover quality as there is little information available to relate cover characteristics and habitat value.

Turbulence and wood size classes are flexible and could be redefined for any specific habitat assessment program. Develop documentation for the specific criteria chosen.

The sampling design recommended here matches the one used for substrate assessment, so both sets of habitat attributes could be recorded simultaneously. See the pebble count technique (Chapter 9, section 9.4) for related information.

The characteristics of aquatic vegetation depend on season. Therefore, it is advised that the sampling season be standardized to improve comparability of data through time.

Water body: New Creek
Date:
Field investigators:
Study area location:

Transect and section design notes:

Number of transects: 12
Section length: 1 m
Number of sections surveyed: 46
Concealing water depth: 35 cm

Tr. #	Sec. #	Turbulence 5-10	11-40	41-75	>75	Wood 1-5	6-10	11-50	>51	Vegetation Dist. (m)	Class	Notes and depth
1	1							2	1	0.4	Emergent	
1	2		1					1		0		
1	3			1						0		
1	4					3	2			0.3	Submerged	
1	5											Incomplete
2	1				1					0		
2	2									0		Deep water
2	3		1					1		0		
2	4	1				1				0.2	Submerged	
2	5					3	1			0.9	Submerged	
3	1	1								0		
3	2	1								0		Deep water
3	3		1							0		
3	4			1						0	Submerged	
3	5				1				1	0	Submerged	
3	6			1						0		
3	7					1	1			0.5	Emergent	
4	1	.	.	.	.	.	.	.	.	.	.	.
4	2	.	.	.	.	.	.	.	.	.	.	.
.	.	.	.	.	.	.	.	.	.	.	.	.
.	.	.	.	.	.	.	.	.	.	.	.	.
.	.	.	.	.	.	.	.	.	.	.	.	.
.	.	.	.	.	.	.	.	.	.	.	.	.
.	.	.	.	.	.	.	.	.	.	.	.	.
.	.	.	.	.	.	.	.	.	.	.	.	.
12	46	9	15	8	5	21	15	11	4	10.4	Submerged	8 Deep sections

Figure 10.1   Cover composition and abundance data sheet with some sample entries for a stream site assessment.

10.3 Structural Complexity

10.3.1 Rationale

Fish cover is provided by objects or structures that add topographic complexity to a flat habitat bottom. A measure of the deviation from a flat bottom would then be directly related to the amount of underwater structure. Luckhurst and Luckhurst (1978) provided a simple field technique to quantify deviation from a flat habitat. The technique compares the straight-line distance between fixed points with the bottom contour distance, including objects that add structure such as logs and boulders. The more structured the habitat, the greater the distance between two fixed points. This technique can be used when there is a variety of structures (including nonbiological debris such as tires) because the measurements detect anything that interrupts a flat habitat bottom. The technique has been adapted from its original form to be used along transects and sections in shallow habitats.

10.3.2 Preparation

▶ Select the length of transect sections to be used prior to actual field measurements. Because a ratio of lengths rather than absolute distances is used as final data, the transect section lengths can be changed from assessment site to site (not within sites or samples). Linear transect section lengths should be at least 2 m long so that distance changes due to cover objects on the transect can be easily measured.

▶ Obtain one or more chains or heavily weighted (lead-core) and flexible ropes, a standard length rope that corresponds to transect section lengths, and stakes and flags for marking transect positions and section endpoints.

10.3.3 Procedures

■ **Arrange transects.** Locate a series of transects to representatively sample shallow-water (depths at which the substrate is visible) habitats at the lake or stream assessment site. The zig-zag transect arrangement described above (section 10.2.3) can be used or transects can parallel the shoreline: narrow streams (<5 m wide) should have a transect situated 1 m off each shore and one or two transects evenly spaced in midstream; for wide streams, add midstream transects parallel to shore but at increasing distances from shore in shallow water. Divide transects into equal-length sections that are at least 2-m long so that 15 or more sections are available for measurement.

■ **Measure linear and contour lengths.** For each transect section, mark the section endpoints with stakes or flags on shore, or have two people stand the specified distance apart in the water. This is the linear distance between section endpoints. Position a chain or weighted (lead-core) rope along the transect section length and allow the chain to follow the substrate contours and hang over logs and other objects. Mark the transect section endpoints on the chain by grasping these points with the hand or attaching a clip of some kind. Remove the chain from the water and on shore measure the length between marks to obtain the contour length. Repeat the measurement of contour lengths along all transect sections.

■ **Compute ratio values.** Calculate the ratio of contour length to linear length for each transect. Values close to one denote relatively simple topography, and higher values indicate topographically complex sites. The ratio for each transect section is the substrate ratio, and a mean of all sets of measurements provides a single measure of structural complexity for the assessment site.

10.3.4 Notes

This technique requires snorkeling in water deeper than 2 m because it is important to determine the exact endpoints of the contour measurements.

This technique is not descriptive of the type of cover (i.e., wood debris, vegetation, bank structures, etc.). Notes regarding the types of cover detected in the survey would make the technique more helpful.

10.4 Cover Density

10.4.1 Rationale

The cover density technique (Kinsolving and Bain 1990) enumerates objects that bisect a plane extending from the water surface to the habitat bottom for each transect section. It describes all of the instream cover and refuge regardless of whether it is wood debris, vegetation, boulders, or overhanging structures in the water. The technique is simple and does no more than provide counts of nonsubstrate objects. Large counts are associated with high cover density. The counting process can initially be confusing because rules determine what should be counted, but with experience the technique is rapid and easy to understand.

10.4.2 Preparation

▶ Obtain one or more heavily weighted (lead core) ropes to guide counting along a transect section, and some stakes and flagging for marking transect positions and section endpoints.

10.4.3 Procedure

▪ **Arrange transects.** Locate a series of transects to sample shallow water (depths at which the substrate is visible) habitats at the lake or stream assessment site. Use the zig-zag transect arrangement described in section 10.2.3 or the shoreline parallel transect arrangement described in section 10.3.3. Divide transects into sections that are equal length and at least 0.5 m long, so that 50 or more sections are available for cover counts. Transect section lengths can be about any length but they should be sized so that cover object counts are not so large as to be confusing (>25). Final results will be reported in counts per linear transect distance so varying the section lengths per site will not make sites incomparable.

▪ **Count cover objects per section.** Begin at one end of the transect section, and count the number of surfaces encountering a plane that extends from the water surface to the stream bottom. Counts can be done visually or by touching objects above the substrate in the plane. Exclude the actual stream bottom from your counts or any substrate particle including boulders. Rules for counting the number of surfaces are:

• solid objects with a diameter greater than 10 cm, are counted as two surfaces;

• objects with a diameter less than 10 cm are counted as a single surface;

• objects located closer than 3 cm to each other are counted as one surface;

• portions of a cover object that are geometrically separate (such as branches on a tree) are counted separately;

• undercut banks are considered to be cover objects, and are therefore counted.

Figure 10.2 shows an example of counting surfaces on a section plane. Record the number of object surfaces that intersect each section plane.

▪ **Compute site results.** After all sections are counted, compute cover density (mean counts per transect length, e.g., 0.7/m) by summing all counts, the number of sections counted, and the total linear length included in all counts. Other statistics can be computed such as the percent of sections with cover of some kind (nonzero counts) and variance of the counts as an index of cover dispersion.

10.4.4 Notes

Although the counting rules can be modified to fit assessment program needs, the rules cannot be changed among sites. Any counting rules need to be well documented. For instance, if adult salmonids are of special interest, the size limitations for adequate cover must be increased to match the size of the adult fish; whereas, if juvenile fish are of special interest, then the size limitations should be decreased because a juvenile fish can find adequate cover in small spaces.

This technique may not be very accurate in areas where there is either significant floating vegetation or where the stream or lake bottom is covered with fine but dense vegetation. In such cases, the rules would dictate that each increment would only be given a score of one, and underestimates of cover would therefore occur. In such cases it is recommended that surveyors use the technique to assess aquatic vegetation cover outlined in section 10.2.

This technique is not descriptive of the type of cover (i.e., wood debris, vegetation, bank structures, etc.). Notes about the types of cover detected in the survey could enhance this technique.

In the cover density technique, counts are not adjusted for variation in water depth among sections. Therefore, cover is not counted based on habitat volume. We assume deep water provides cover and counts are limited to shallow water so some of the potential shortcoming of ignoring depth should be reduced. Nevertheless, this technique may not satisfy assessment needs for habitat where cover per habitat volume is of special interest or target fish species respond strongly to cover depth distribution.

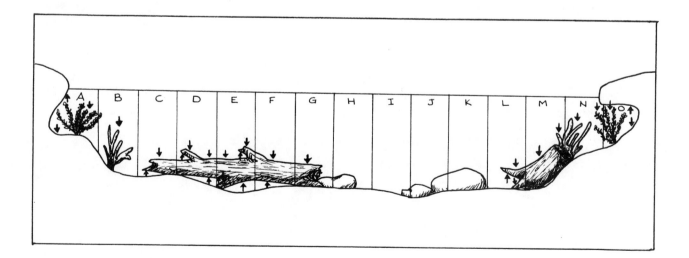

Figure 10.2   Example of counting surfaces on transect section planes for the cover density technique.

Streambank and Shoreline Condition

11

Nathalie J. Stevenson and Katherine E. Mills

11.1 Introduction

11.1.1 Background

Streambanks and lake shores are important transition zones between aquatic and terrestrial systems. When in good condition, these habitats are well vegetated, resistant to erosion, and provide cover and refuge for fish species in various life stages. Human impacts and natural disturbances reduce bank vegetation, erosion resistance, structural stability, and fish cover value. Shoreline fish cover is degraded when bank vegetation is lost and elevated erosion rates lead to undercut banks that collapse quickly when banks erode. Inputs of sediment and silt to lakes and streams reduce water transparency, smother fish eggs and benthos, and fill pools and shallow water habitats. Bank condition is assessed by evaluating the attributes associated with erosion rates and structural stability: bank height, root depth, percent root density, bank angle, percent surface protection (bank cover), and the composition of substrate and soil. The techniques described below rate the condition of streambank and shoreline habitats, measure physical attributes indicative of condition, and document degradation of bank habitat by agricultural animal use.

11.1.2 Selection of Techniques

This chapter describes techniques for assessing streambank and shoreline condition visually and by using instruments. The technique for rating streambank and shoreline cover incorporates an evaluation of vegetation and rock cover associated with stable, low erosion habitats. Measurement of streambank angle and undercutting reflects erosion rates and stability, but this technique is especially relevant for documenting undercut habitats used by select species (e.g., salmonids). The technique for rating animal use damage has limited utility, but this form of habitat impact is important and pervasive in many parts of North America. The latter two specialized techniques are of interest in regions where undercut banks support key species or animal damage to stream habitat is a problem. A comprehensive evaluation of streambank and shoreline condition could be done by pairing a specialized technique with the more general cover assessment technique. Bank shape and animal damage can then be linked to information on erodible banks and shores.

11.2 Streambank and Shoreline Cover

11.2.1 Rationale

Streambank and shoreline stability is influenced by the erosion resistance role of plant roots and bank rock. Vegetation and large boulders stabilize banks and protect them from erosion when inundated: living root systems hold soil in place; increased roughness slows local water velocity; and surface vegetation can promote sediment deposition (Myers 1989). Trees and shrubs have deeper and larger root systems than grasses and forbs; however, a heterogeneous variety of plants provide greater bank stability than monotypic plant communities. With this technique both the amount of rooted vegetation and the amount of rocky ground cover are assessed using a measure of total bank cover to evaluate the susceptibility of banks to erosion. The basic method applies to both lentic and lotic waters, although the procedure is described for streams and modifications are suggested for lakes and reservoirs. Use this method to derive a total bank cover assessment that corresponds with erosion potential and stability. The methods used for lentic and for lotic environments are based on Pfankuch (1975) and Hamilton and Bergerson (1984).

11.2.2 Preparation

▶ Plan for the arrangement of transects along streambanks or lake shore. For streams, have an estimate of average stream width for selecting transect and segment lengths.

▶ Acquire measuring tape, stakes and flagging to define segments, and data recording sheets.

11.2.3 Procedures

■ **Arrange stream site survey.** At base flow during summer or early fall, arrange one transect midway between the water edge and the floodplain (level land adjacent to the stream and inundated less than annually) running roughly parallel to the water edge. The length of the transect should be between five and seven times the average channel width of the stream. Once the transect has been established, mark 30 or more points with stakes or flagging along the transect length at regularly spaced intervals (e.g., every 5 m). These points define transect segments or the transect lengths between points.

■ **Rate transect segments.** The observer should start at one end of the transect and determine ratings (1–4) for vegetation cover and rocky cover (ratings defined in Table 11.1) by transect segment (example on field form in Figure 11.1). Ratings for vegetation and rock cover should be recorded separately.

■ **Calculate site results.** For each transect, compute mean bank scores separately for vegetation and rocky cover by multiplying the rating values by the number of observations and dividing the sum of products by the number of transect segments. Figure 11.1 shows a sample data sheet with entries and calculations for one transect. For each transect, take the whole value (drop fractions) of the mean scores for vegetation and rocky material ratings and sum them. Compare the sum to the total cover rating in Table 11.1. Enter the final total cover rating for the transect as in Figure 11.1. The right and left bank transects could be averaged or reported separately for the assessment site.

■ **Modifications for lakes and reservoirs.** This technique can be easily adapted for use on lake and reservoir shorelines. Transects should be deployed to sample the area of interest or dispersed around the water body if the assessment is intended to represent the entire shoreline. Position the transect parallel to the shoreline within the zone between high and low lake levels. For reservoirs, position the transects along the summer pool level or in the zone between high and low summer pool levels. Do not apply the technique in the drawdown zone of seasonally regulated reservoirs because terrestrial vegetation cannot persist in this habitat. The field form shown in Figure 11.1 will need to be modified for the number of transects used.

11.3 Bank Shape

11.3.1 Rationale

Shoreline habitats are important for many fish species and life stages, and shoreline shape is related to bank erosion rates. Gradually sloping banks indicate stable lake and stream margins because they are less vulnerable to sloughing and they are formed by slow erosion and sediment deposition rates. Steep and undercut banks indicate accelerated erosion associated with intensive land use and shoreline disturbances like livestock grazing, although some bank undercutting is expected even in pristine waters. Undercut banks are valuable

Table 11.1   Rating criteria for vegetation cover, rocky cover, and total cover for transect segments along streambanks (modified from Hamilton and Bergersen 1984).

Rating value	Criteria and description
	Vegetation cover

4   Combined cover of trees, shrubs, grass and forbs is greater than 90% of the transect segment. Openings in this nearly complete cover are small and dispersed. Many plant species and age classes are represented. Growth is vigorous and the age or size structure of plants suggests continued ground cover. A deep, dense root mass is likely.

3   Plants cover 70–90% of the transect segment. Shrub species are more prevalent than trees. Openings in the tree canopy are larger than the space resulting from the loss of a single mature individual. Although plant growth appears good, few or no large and old trees and shrubs are present. A deep root mass may not seem continuous, and significant erosion is possible in the openings during high streamflow.

2   Plant cover ranges from 50 to 70% of the transect segment. Lack of vigor is evident in some individuals or species. Tree seedling reproduction is nil. Much of the transect segment lacks vegetation with the potential for a deep root mass. Serious erosion is likely at high streamflows.

1   Less than 50% of the segment is covered by vegetation. Trees are rare or absent, and shrub cover is sparse and clumped. Growth and reproduction vigor is generally poor. Root mass is likely to be discontinuous and shallow.

Rocky material cover

4   Rock makes up 65% or more of the transect segment, and large boulders (longest axis >30 cm) are numerous.

3   The transect segment is 40–65% rocky material: mostly small boulders and cobble 15–30 cm across.

2   The transect segment is 20–40% rocky material. Although some small boulders may be present, most are 8–15 cm across.

1   Less than 20% of segment is stony material, mostly gravel 2.5–8 cm across.

Total cover rating

≥4   Excellent   Nearly all of the streambank is covered by vegetation in vigorous condition or by boulders and cobble.

4   Good   Most of the streambank surfaces are covered by vegetation or rocky material the size of pebbles and larger. Areas not covered by vegetation are protected by materials that will limit erosion at high streamflows.

3   Fair   A substantial portion of the streambank surface is not covered by vegetation or rocky material. These areas are have poor resistance to erosion.

2   Poor   Little of the streambank surface is covered by vegetation or rocky material, and there is little or no resistance to erosion. Banks are clearly eroded each year by high streamflows.

Assessment Site:	
Recorder:	Date and time:
Streamflow condition:	

Streambank Cover Form

Right	Veg.	Rock
1	1	3
2	3	2
3	2	2
4	1	3
5	1	2
6	1	1
7	1	1
8	2	1
9	4	1
10	1	4
11	1	3
12	1	4
13	4	1
14	1	2
15	1	1
16	1	1
17	2	3
18	1	1
19	2	2
20	2	1
21	3	2
22	4	1
23	1	4
24	4	1
25	4	1
26	4	1
27	3	2
28	3	2
29	4	1
30	4	1
31	1	2
32	1	2
33		
34		
35		

Left	Veg.	Rock
1		
2		
3		
4		
5		
6		
7		
8		
9		
10		
11		
12		
13		
14		
15		
16		
17		
18		
19		
20		
21		
22		
23		
24		
25		
26		
27		
28		
29		
30		
31		
32		
33		
34		
35		

Right Bank Vegetation

Value	Obser.	Product
1	15	15
2	5	10
3	4	12
4	8	32
	32	69

Mean score = 2.15

Right Bank Rock

Value	Obser.	Product
1	15	15
2	10	20
3	4	12
4	3	12
	32	59

Mean score = 1.84

Left Bank Vegetation

Value	Obser.	Product

Mean score =

Left Bank Rock

Value	Obser.	Product

Mean score =

Right Bank Total Cover Rating:		*Fair*
Veg = 2	Rock = 1	Sum = 3

Right Bank Total Cover Rating:		
Veg =	Rock =	Sum =

Notes on streambanks:

Figure 11.1   Sample streambank cover data sheet showing ratings for the right bank and the associated calculations.

habitats that conceal fish close to currents and often support high, localized fish biomass (Duff et al. 1989). Therefore, characterizing streambank and shoreline shape serves dual purposes of assessing potentially valuable fish habitat and assessing habitats that are sensitive to disturbances including landscape scale processes. Inferring the overall quality of shoreline habitats is possible when data on shoreline morphology is combined with other habitat assessment information like substrate quality, suspended sediment concentrations, and riparian vegetation. The technique described below will provide simple measurements of streambank and shoreline shape for use with other habitat assessment results.

11.3.2 Preparation

▶ Plan for the arrangement of transects along streambanks or sampling locations along lake shores. For streams, have an approximate estimate of average stream width for selecting transect and segment lengths.

▶ Acquire metal meter sticks, long straight edge devices, stakes and flagging to define sample points, data sheets, and a clinometer for measuring angles.

11.3.3 Procedures

■ **Arrange stream site survey.** At base flow of summer or early fall, select a length of stream at least five to seven times the average channel width. Identify evenly spaced (e.g., every 5 m) measurement points that will provide 10 or more recordings per transect.

■ **Measuring bank angle for sloping shorelines.** Using a clinometer and a straight edge, measure the angle at the water edge as shown in Figure 11.2. The angle is determined by placing the clinometer on the straight edge oriented along the bank slope at the water edge. Record the angle of the bank by subtracting the clinometer reading from 180°. For example, in Figure 11.2 the clinometer reads 35°, so the recording is 145°. Note that a vertical wall at the water edge would be recorded as 90°, so slopes less steep will be between 90° and 180°. Record water depth at the water edge as zero and undercut distance as zero (Figure 11.3) to be consistent with measurements for undercut banks explained below.

■ **Measurements for undercut banks.** Three measurements are recorded for undercut banks: bank angle, undercut distance, and water depth at the overhang edge of the undercut. Again using a clinometer and a straight surface, measure the angle of the undercut as shown in Figure 11.4. Position the end of the straight edge at the furthest extent of the undercut as in Figure 11.3 and

Figure 11.2   Using a clinometer to measure a bank angle along a gradually sloping shoreline. The clinometer reading in this case is 35° so the recorded angle will be 145° (from Platts et al. 1987; Filipeck et al. 1994).

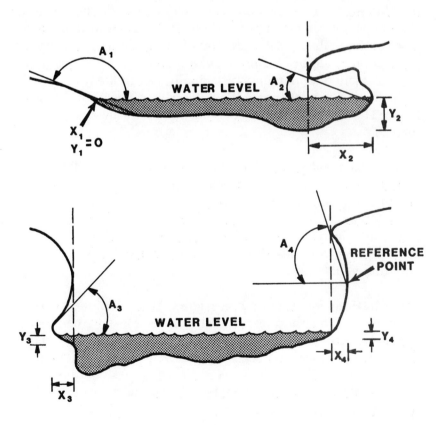

Figure 11.3   Hypothetical channel cross sections illustrating bank angle (A_i), undercut distance (X_i), and water depths (Y_i). (From Platts et al. 1987.)

Figure 11.4   Using a clinometer to measure the angle of an undercut bank. The clinometer reading in this case is 45° and the angle is recorded as 45° (from Platts et al. 1987; Filipeck et al. 1994).

lift the straight edge to the underside of the undercut land surface. Measure this angle and record the same angle shown on the clinometer (i.e., do not subtract from 180°). Also record the distance between the land-inward end of the straight edge and the furthest outer edge of the undercut as in Figure 11.3 to obtain a measurement of undercut depth. Finally, record the water depth at the point directly beneath the outer edge of the undercut as in Figure 11.3. Note that undercut bank angles are always less than 90°.

■ **Summarize results.** A series of bank measurements will usually include some sloping shorelines and undercut banks. All bank and undercut angles can be averaged to obtain a mean shore angle (range >0° to <180°). Water depths and undercut depths can be averaged for undercut bank measurements (angles <90°). These mean values describe the typical fish habitat associated with undercut banks.

■ **Modifications for lakes and reservoirs.** This technique can be easily used on lake and reservoir shorelines. Measurement points should be deployed to sample the area of interest or dispersed evenly around the water body if the assessment is intended to represent the entire shoreline. For reservoirs, position the transects along the summer pool level or in the zone between high and low summer pool levels.

11.3.4 Notes

Evenly spaced bank measurements across an assessment site yield data on typical bank shape, but this sampling design may miss undercut bank habitat when it is sparse along a stream or lake. Measurements aimed at undercut bank habitat can be made but it should be noted on any field forms and database entries that these measurements were targeted at the particular habitat.

Platts et al. (1987) reported that year to year precision and accuracy are good for streambank angles greater than 90° because the 95% confidence intervals around the means are quite narrow. However, the 95% confidence intervals around the means of bank undercut are wide since the two points that define the undercut measurements are difficult to accurately determine in the field.

The actual bank angle should be recorded in the field, however, it may be useful to categorize the angles (or average values if applicable) to aid data interpretation. The following classification criteria are recommended: less than 90° indicates undercut banks; 90° to 135° indicates steeply sloping shorelines; and greater than 135° reflects gently sloping banks.

11.4   Shoreline Animal Damage

11.4.1 Rationale

Many streams flow through agricultural range or pasture land, and it is common for cattle, horses, and sheep to graze on streambanks. Intensive animal use of streamside areas often results in destabilized streambanks, sloughing and mass erosion of bank material, trampling of edge habitats, and consumption of riparian vegetation. The resulting habitat damage can be severe, and management intervention may be required to limit loss and restore bank habitat. The technique described below provides a rapid and easy way to qualitatively assess the effect of livestock use on the local streambanks. The technique was not intended for use in lake and reservoir habitat assessments.

11.4.2 Preparation

▶ Plan for the arrangement of transects along streambanks. Have an approximate estimate of average stream width for selecting transect and segment lengths.

▶ Acquire measuring tape, stakes and flagging to define segments, and data recording sheets.

11.4.3 Procedure

■ **Arrange site survey.** Follow the procedure described in section 11.2.3 for locating transects divided into segments. The transect segments serve here as units of observation for rating the extent of animal damage to streambanks.

- **Rate animal damage by transect segment.** At each transect segment, note whether the land adjacent to the stream is used for livestock grazing; if so, assess the level of livestock use and associated damage, and record the rating values (Table 11.2).

- **Summarize results.** Animal damage ratings can be summarized with simple statistics (mean and range of ratings) for both banks or separately.

Table 11.2   Transect segment rating criteria for animal damage assessment (modified from Duff et al. 1989).

Rating value		Criteria and description
4	Undamaged	Little or no evidence of streambank damage and evidence of animal use limited to 10–25% of the segment length. Little or no bank erosion or sloughing. Vegetative plant biomass at or near natural conditions.
3	Moderate damage	Streambank has evidence of animal damage in 26–50% of the segment length. Some erosion and sloughing evident. Less than half of potential plant biomass remains on site.
2	High damage	Streambank has evidence of animal damage over 51–75% of the segment length. Moderate to high bank erosion and sloughing during season of animal use and continuing during nonuse period. Annual recovery of vegetation structure limited to a minor portion of the segment.
1	Excessive damage	Streambank has evidence of animal damage over 76–100% of the segment length. Severe bank erosion and sloughing occurring over most or all to the segment streambank since root system and stem mass completely damaged. No evidence of bank recovery and erosion appears constant.

Riparian Vegetation

12

Katherine E. Mills and Nathalie J. Stevenson

12.1 Introduction

12.1.1 Background

A riparian zone is the area adjacent to a watercourse. Stream sides, river floodplain margins, and the edge habitat of lakes, ponds, and other bodies of water are all riparian zones. There are no clear criteria for delineating riparian zones, and Armantrout (1998) defines these habitats as terrestrial areas where the vegetation complex and microclimate conditions are products of the presence and influence of perennial or intermittent water. The extent of a riparian zone can be identified by changes in vegetation related to soil moisture. Riparian areas often support complex plant communities associated with diverse soil and hydrological variation (Platts et al. 1987), and typically including mature forest, low alder, brush, grasses, marshes, and agricultural pasture or fields. A variety of shrubs and long-lived tree species will grow in healthy riparian zones. Riparian vegetation is important to the input of nutrient and organic matter, the source of large woody debris, fish food and cover, the interception and storage of solar energy, reduction in solar heating, attenuation of flood flow scouring forces, and moderation of terrestrial nutrient inputs from agricultural sources (Myers 1989). An assessment of riparian vegetation composition and structure provides useful management information.

There are many techniques that evaluate vegetation to assess the status of riparian habitats; examples are Cowardin et al. (1979) for the U.S. Fish and Wildlife Service, Duff et al. (1989) for the Bureau of Land Management, Hansen et al. (1995) for Montana, and Swanson et al. (1988) for Nevada. Some methods directly assess vegetation, while others are based on soil and physical conditions.

Directly evaluating riparian vegetation requires examining community types, species composition, canopy cover, tree crown width, vegetation density, shadow characteristics, root depth and root density, and even areal coverage of each layer of vegetation. This chapter describes techniques that can be used to directly assess vegetation composition and structure in the riparian zone of streams, lakes, and reservoirs.

The most meaningful riparian assessments focus on relations between physical and biological factors influenced by the water–land transition landscape (Naiman et al. 1992). The techniques presented in this chapter characterize the basic structure of the riparian vegetation in height layers and stratify vegetation into understory (herbaceous plants and shrubs) and overstory (trees) layers. The understory has a majority of short-lived plants that revegetate annually; therefore, it provides a good indication of current soil and hydrological conditions. In contrast, trees in the overstory layer are long-lived and persistent plant community members that reflect long-term conditions.

12.1.2 Selection of Techniques

The assessment of riparian vegetation, like any plant assemblage analysis, can be complicated and time consuming. It is important to select the level of classification needed to meet management objectives. For example, would structure-level information be sufficient or are species-level data required? This chapter provides a general (section 12.2) vegetation characterization technique, as well as a more detailed (section 12.3) classification technique that focuses only on the area adjacent to the water body of interest. The techniques vary mainly in level of detail, measurement precision, and spatial scope. These techniques can be used to classify vegetation by category or by species. The technique provided in section 12.3 (water side vegetation assessment) requires identifying plant species and is appropriate for an in-depth description of vegetation composition and structure.

12.2 General Vegetation Characterization

12.2.1 Rationale

Vegetation structure reflects many important riparian site characteristics and functions, and riparian sites with diverse vegetation will have generally greater habitat value (Myers 1989). However, different vegetation types contribute to aquatic systems in different ways: large trees contribute wood, shade, and allochthonous inputs; shrubs stabilize banks and make it possible for solar radiation to penetrate the water. A general assessment of vegetation composition and vertical structure can be conducted quickly and easily by using the techniques described in this section. Using growth form (herbaceous, shrub, tree) to assess cover does not require expertise in identifying plant species.

12.2.2 Preparation

▶ Obtain field forms, one or more tape measures, a telescoping surveyors rod, and some stakes and flagging to mark transects.

12.2.3 Procedures

■ **Arrange transects and points.** Locate five or more transects extending outward from the streambank or lakeshore bank (not the water edge) approximately 10 m or to the outer edge of the riparian zone (transition to uplands or vegetation unrelated to water body). Transects can be evenly spaced to cover the assessment site and should be perpendicular to the bank. For stream assessments place five or more transects on each side of the stream or river. Mark the transects as left or right bank on the data sheet (sample shown in Figure 12.1). Identify 100 points at even intervals on all the transects. Select a length interval that results in about 20 points per transect or 100 for the assessment site. Maintain the same spacing between points on all transects rather than forcing the same number of points on transects of different lengths.

■ **Characterize vegetation composition.** For each transect, designate on a form (as in Figure 12.1) the classes of vegetation that constitute a majority of the cover (primary vegetation component) and the classes of vegetation that constitute significant but secondary components of cover. The classes of vegetation are listed in Figure 12.1 (forbs, grasses, shrubs, etc.). Forbs are broadleaved herbaceous plants, grasses are narrow leaved, and both lack woody stems above ground. Shrubs are woody plants that are typically bushy and less than 6 m tall at maturity (Cowardin 1979; e.g., speckled alder *Alnus rugosa* or buttonbush *Cephalanthus occidentalis*). Definitions for wetland classes are in Armantrout (1998).

■ **Measure vegetation cover by height.** For each transect point, extend a telescoping survey rod from the ground up to the maximum extension of herbaceous plant height (this may vary but should not be more than 1.5 m). Record whether or not the rod hits herbaceous vegetation by placing an H in the box (Figure 12.1) for the sampling point. Record an H once per sample point even if herbaceous vegetation touches the rod at several points. Next, extend the rod upwards to the maximum extension of shrub height (usually about 6 m). Record whether or not the rod hits shrub vegetation by placing an S in the box (Figure 12.1) for the sampling point. Next, extend the rod up to tree height and record whether or not the rod hits tree vegetation by placing a T

Riparian Vegetation Characterization

	Assessment Site:	
	Recorder:	Date and time:
	Streamflow/lake level condition:	

Transect	1	2	3	4	5	6	7	8	9	10
Bare soil										
Forbs										
Grasses, sedges, rushes										
Shrubs										
Trees with deciduous, broadleaf overstory										
Trees, with perennial overstorey										
Wetland vegetation Bog										
Fen										
Marsh										
Agricultural vegetation Row crops										
Grasses, forbs										
Pasture, grazed cover										

Entries: 1 = primary components of cover, 2 = secondary components of cover.

Site design notes:

Right bank transects:

Left bank transects:

Lake or reservoir site

Vegetation notes:

Point Intercept Recordings

Enter in each box:

H for Herbaceous

S for Shrub

T for Tree

— empty sample points

Right bank pts:

Herbaceous cover:

H entries:

% cover:

Shrub cover:

S entries:

% cover:

Tree cover:

T entries:

% cover:

Left bank pts:

Herbaceous cover:

H entries:

% cover:

Shrub cover:

S entries:

% cover:

Tree cover:

T entries:

% cover:

Figure 12.1 Example riparian vegetation characterization field form for designating primary and secondary vegetation by transect, and recording vegetation intercepts at sampling points.

in the box (Figure 12.1) for the sampling point. When tree height exceeds rod length, an observer could use the survey rod to visually estimate if tree vegetation intersects the sampling point. Finally, place a dash in the boxes for sampling points that had no vegetation recorded so the number of sampling points are clearly shown on the data sheet. Calculate the percentage of sampling points with each type of vegetation by dividing the number of entries (H, S, T separately) by the total number of point measurements taken (at least 100). The results are percent cover for each vegetation height category. Figure 12.1 shows a sample data sheet for recording frequency and percent cover calculations.

12.2.4 Notes

The end of the riparian zone may be inconsistently identified among field staff as there are no riparian delineation rules.

The vegetation classes (e.g., shrubs, trees) are broad so that there is less chance of observer error and field tasks are simplified. More detailed assessment would use height categories or record heights of plant intercepts with sampling points.

Sampling must be done during the summer because plant growth and coverage varies seasonally.

A spherical densiometer could be used to more precisely measure canopy cover for trees (described below).

12.3 **Water Side Vegetation Assessment**

12.3.1 Rationale

Some habitat assessment programs require more detailed information on riparian vegetation than can be obtained from the general characterization technique. Swanson et al. (1988) developed a vegetation classification system that integrates information on vegetation, soils, and hydrology, and can be applied easily and quickly. The Swanson et al. (1988) technique is based on observation, but when it is combined with the use of a spherical densiometer, quantitative vegetation cover data are obtained. Because of the densiometer, this technique presented is most accurate for plants more than 10 m in height. The technique described was adapted from Swanson et al. (1988) to simplify their riparian community classification and to eliminate material that is covered by techniques in other chapters of this manual. Although the Swanson et al. (1988) technique was developed for streams, we outline some minor steps that make it applicable to reservoir and lake shorelines.

12.3.2 Preparation

▶ Field staff should develop knowledge of the common riparian plant species, as well as basic soil types and formation processes present in the area.

▶ Obtain taxonomic guides to regional flora, sample bags and labels for unidentified species, a spherical densiometer, one or more tape measures, some stakes and flagging, and waterproof data sheets (sample in Figure 12.2).

▶ Modify a standard spherical densiometer as shown in Figure 12.3 so it records directional rather than 360° views (as in Platts et al. 1987).

12.3.3 Procedures

■ **Identify sampling points.** Data are to be recorded at each end of a habitat assessment site. For streams, at each end of the site set up a transect across the stream channel with endpoints on each bank. Three locations should be identified and marked along this transect line: one 30 cm out from the right bank, one in midstream, and one 30 cm out from the left bank. For lakes, mark an observation point 30 cm off the shoreline bank at each end of the site or periodically around the lake.

■ **Classify riparian vegetation.** Looking into the riparian zone from each shoreline sampling location, identify and record which of the following three riparian types best describes the habitat (see data sheet in Figure 12.2).

Hydroriparian wetlands have hydric soils or substrates that are rarely or only briefly dry. Vegetation is predominantly obligate and preferential wet riparian plants.

Mesoriparian areas have nonhydric soils and substrates that are dry seasonally. Vegetation is a mixture of obligate, preferential, and facultative riparian plants.

Xeroriparian habitats are mesic to xeric; the average moisture is higher than the surrounding uplands due to occasional (less than one month a year) surface wetting or increased groundwater from the associated water body. Vegetation is preferential, facultative, and nonriparian plants.

After identifying the riparian type, select the dominant class of trees, shrubs, and herbaceous plants (evergreen, deciduous, low, high, mixed) and record information on a data sheet (Figure 12.2). Finally, record the dominant plant taxa for trees, shrubs, and herbaceous vegetation layers. If multiple, similarly important taxa exist in a layer, then list them as codominant taxa using a hyphen to separate the species names.

■ **Quantify cover by vegetation layer.** Use a modified spherical densiometer (Figure 12.3) to measure the extent of cover from tree, shrub, and herbaceous plant layers. At each bank location and midstream point, face the bank, upstream or downstream (upstream and downstream as separate observations) and hold

Assessment Site:		Riparian
Recorder:	Date and time:	Vegetation
Streamflow/lake level condition:		Classification

End of site : upstream __, downstream __, lakeshore at _____

Right Bank or _____

Hydroriparian		Trees	evergreen , deciduous , mixed	Taxa:	
Mesoriparian		Shrubs	tall (> 1m) , low (≤ 1 m) , mixed	Taxa:	
Xeroriparian		Herbaceous	tall (>30 cm) , low (≤30 cm) , mixed	Taxa:	
		Other			

Left Bank

Hydroriparian		Trees	evergreen , deciduous , mixed	Taxa:	
Mesoriparian		Shrubs	tall (> 1m) , low (≤ 1 m) , mixed	Taxa:	
Xeroriparian		Herbaceous	tall (>30 cm) , low (≤30 cm) , mixed	Taxa:	
		Other			

End of site : upstream __, downstream __, lakeshore at _____

Right Bank or _____

Hydroriparian		Trees	evergreen , deciduous , mixed	Taxa:	
Mesoriparian		Shrubs	tall (> 1m) , low (≤ 1 m) , mixed	Taxa:	
Xeroriparian		Herbaceous	tall (>30 cm) , low (≤30 cm) , mixed	Taxa:	
		Other			

Left Bank

Hydroriparian		Trees	evergreen , deciduous , mixed	Taxa:	
Mesoriparian		Shrubs	tall (> 1m) , low (≤ 1 m) , mixed	Taxa:	
Xeroriparian		Herbaceous	tall (>30 cm) , low (≤30 cm) , mixed	Taxa:	
		Other			

Spherical Densiometer

End of site : upstream __, downstream __, lakeshore at _____

Right bank or:	Trees	points of	=	% cover
	Shrubs	points of	=	% cover
	Herbaceous	points of	=	% cover
Middle, upstream	Trees	points of	=	% cover
	Shrubs	points of	=	% cover
	Herbaceous	points of	=	% cover
Middle, downstream	Trees	points of	=	% cover
	Shrubs	points of	=	% cover
	Herbaceous	points of	=	% cover
Left bank	Trees	points of	=	% cover
	Shrubs	points of	=	% cover
	Herbaceous	points of	=	% cover

End of site : upstream __, downstream __, lakeshore at _____

Right bank or:	Trees	points of	=	% cover
	Shrubs	points of	=	% cover
	Herbaceous	points of	=	% cover
Middle, upstream	Trees	points of	=	% cover
	Shrubs	points of	=	% cover
	Herbaceous	points of	=	% cover
Middle, downstream	Trees	points of	=	% cover
	Shrubs	points of	=	% cover
	Herbaceous	points of	=	% cover
Left bank	Trees	points of	=	% cover
	Shrubs	points of	=	% cover
	Herbaceous	points of	=	% cover

Figure 12.2   Example riparian vegetation classification field form for recording the composition of plant layers along a water course, and measuring canopy cover with a densiometer.

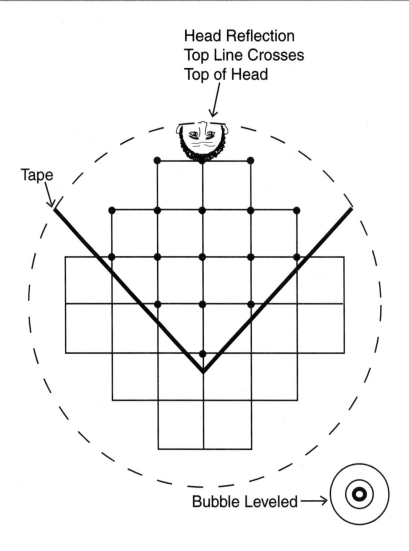

Figure 12.3   The concave spherical densiometer with placement of head reflection, bubble level, tape, and 17 observation points. Figure and device alterations are from Platts et al. (1987).

the densiometer about 30 cm above the land or water surface. The arm between the hand to the elbow should be horizontal to the water surface. The instrument should be held away from the observer with the bottom of the 'V' pointed towards the recorder so that his or her head reflection almost touches the top of the grid line. Level the densiometer with the bubble level in the viewfinder, and count the number of intercepts above the 'V' taped on the densiometer (Figure 12.3) hit by either herbaceous plants, shrubs, or trees. Record the number of intercepting points for each vegetation level (i.e., the frequency) on a data form (Figure 12.2). To calculate the percent cover, divide the total number of densiometer points recorded for each vegetation layer by the number sampled (often 17, 37, or 96 depending on the densiometer) and multiply by 100.

12.3.4 Notes

This technique avoids the problem of unclear riparian zone boundaries by assessing riparian areas from the water body perspective; water edge vegetation is evaluated.

In most plant communities, the taxa attain their maximal seasonal development at different times (Daubenmire 1959). If estimating cover by species, it may be necessary to sample multiple times in the growing season. Otherwise, sampling should occur during the summer when vegetation grouped by level is much less effected by seasonal growth patterns.

The curved, reflecting surface of a spherical densiometer typically has 37 intersections that form 24 squares, although some densiometers have 96 intersections. The curved surface results in observations from lateral as well as overhead positions, and consequently an overlap of readings would occur with the recommended sampling design. To account for this, Platts et al. (1987) devised a modification (taping the sphere surface) to isolate 17 intersections as observation points (Figure 12.3).

Barriers

13

Anne S. Gallagher

13.1 Introduction

13.1.1 Background

Physical barriers in streams and rivers are any structures or habitat conditions that create a potential obstacle to fish migration. Migratory fish rely on free passage through streams and rivers to spawn, reach rearing areas, seek food supplies, and satisfy other life requirements. Barriers can impede or even eliminate the movement of fish, disrupting their life cycle and limiting populations. Barriers can also influence stream life by disrupting flow, sediment transport, and thermal regimes. The effects that barriers can have on stream communities vary widely with the type and size of barrier.

Large dams have the greatest detrimental effect on streams, and their influence has been well documented (Ward and Stanford 1979; Baxter and Glaude 1980; Petts 1984; Williams and Wolman 1984). Small structures are often problematic because it is difficult to identify when a structure is actually a barrier to fish migration. Some fish will easily clear a 3-m waterfall, and yet a 1-m dam will pose a barrier to others. The ability to clear a barrier depends on its physical and hydraulic features, and the biology of the fish or fishes that need to pass by the structure. These factors can work separately or together to prevent fish from passing.

The techniques outlined below describe the steps necessary to quantify the potential of a barrier to block fish migration. Large artificial dams are discussed separately from other barriers because of the great difference in their size and effects. Habitat conditions that act as barriers to fish migration are treated separately because they do not involve any structure. Note that this chapter focuses on the ability of a barrier to limit fish movements. Barriers can have enormous influence on the ecology of streams and rivers, but these effects are not discussed here. To quantify biotic and abiotic changes in a stream due to a barrier (e.g., temperature changes, stream geomorphology changes), consult the other chapters in this book that address the specific factors of interest.

13.1.2 Selection of Techniques

The techniques below provide the means to identify and substantiate fish movement impediments that would be considered barriers. This set of techniques covers very different types of barriers: natural and small artificial structures, large dams, and stream habitat conditions. One or more techniques should be selected to fit the assessment situation. When unsure which technique is most appropriate, the relations between fish swimming and jumping performance in the first and third techniques can be used to determine which assessment is most relevant.

13.2 Assessing Natural and Small Artificial Barriers

13.2.1 Rationale

A structure is only a barrier to fish migration if fish cannot pass the structure. Fish can pass a structure in one of three ways: swim over it, jump over it, or bypass it through a fish ladder or similar facility. Fish can swim over some structures, such as cascades or low-lying dams, if the fish can swim faster than the water flowing over the structure. Fish can jump over a structure if: (1) the maximum jumping height of the fish is greater than the height of the structure, and (2) the pool of water below the structure is deep enough for the fish to reach maximum jump height. Maximum fish jumping height requires a depth of water 1.25 times the height of the structure, but no less than about 2.5 m (Reiser and Peacock 1985). Other factors can also affect barrier potential. Turbulent water below the structure can disorient fish and reduce jumping height. Abnormal temperatures or oxygen levels can reduce fish physiological performance and thus jumping heights. Finally, most migratory fish tire as they migrate, so the further a fish is along its migratory path, the less likely it will be able to jump high. Each of these factors must be considered when determining if a structure is a barrier.

Characteristics of barrier structures must be quantified to determine the likelihood of blocking fish movements. Effects of a structure increase with increasing structure size. Hydraulic features of a structure, such as speed and depth of water flow, are also important and vary with structure size. The dimensions of the barrier and its associated hydraulic features provide crucial information for judging how significant a structure is in blocking fish movement. The technique below provides steps to quantify fish performance and structure attributes to determine the likelihood that a structure is a fish barrier. This technique is appropriate for assessment of small natural and artificial structures.

13.2.2 Preparation

▶ Develop familiarity with barrier structures, standard measurements, and use of hydraulic measurement equipment necessary to fill out the data sheet.

▶ Develop thorough knowledge of fish species in the study area.

▶ Obtain a map of the stream, marked in river miles or kilometers. The map should include both the origin of the migrating fish and their final destination.

▶ Acquire measuring tapes; tools to measure the depth of plunge pools, such as a yardstick (shallow) or a weighted graduated cable (deep); and an instrument to measure water velocity (see Chapter 14, Streamflow, for different techniques and equipment). A boat may be needed for large waters.

▶ Duplicate a data recording sheet for field use (sample provided in Box 13.1).

13.2.3 Procedure

■ **Basic description.** Review the types of barrier structures shown in Figure 13.1. Identify the potential barrier structure and record how far it is from the mouth of the stream. Draw a sketch of the stream reach and include the barrier and any prominent natural or constructed (e.g., bridges, roads) features.

■ **Record dimensions.** The potential barrier must be measured under typical seasonal flow for the fish species of interest. For example, measure structure dimensions during typical spring flow conditions to determine if a dam blocks migration of spring run salmon. When assessing general characteristics of a structure for all fish, make measurements under late summer base flow conditions. This is usually the time of low stream discharge, after snow melt and before the leaf fall. Check flow records, if available, to confirm when flow is typically the lowest. Record the following for each potential barrier (see Figure 13.2 for a guide to where measurements should be taken).

  • Vertical height: height from the water surface at the plunge pool to the water level above the structure.

  • Stream width: streambank to streambank distance at the base of the structure.

  • Breadth of water flow: distance between a vertical line drawn where water begins to fall over the structure and a vertical line drawn at the base of the structure.

  • Gradient: determine by dividing the height of the barrier by the breadth of the water flow.

Box 13.1   Sheet for assessing natural and small artificial barriers.

Location _____   River mile from stream or river mouth _____

Date/time _____   Field crew _____

Type of structure _____

Special features _____

Measurements

    height _____   velocity (top) _____   temperature _____

    width _____   velocity (tail) _____   dissolved oxygen _____

    breadth _____   culvert length _____   pH _____

    gradient _____   culvert height/diameter _____   salinity _____

    pool depth _____   culvert width _____

    cascade length _____   turbidity _____

Type of fish(es) _____

Maximum jumping height $(9l)^2/2\,g$, $(g = 9.8 \text{ m/s}^2, 32.2 \text{ ft/s}^2)$ _____

		Yes	No
a.	Is the maximum jumping height of the fish higher than the structure?	☐	☐
b.	Is the darting speed of the fish faster than water flow over the structure?	☐	☐
c.	Is the darting speed of the fish faster than the tail water velocity?	☐	☐
d.	Is the depth of the plunge pool *either* greater than 1.25 times the height of the barrier or more than 2.5 m deep?	☐	☐
e.	Does the plunge pool water have laminar flow within one-third the height of the structure out from the base?	☐	☐
f.	Is the barrier less than halfway along the distance to the spawning ground?	☐	☐
g.	Are other environmental factors, like temperature and oxygen, within ideal range for the fish?	☐	☐
h.	Is the gradient of the cascade steep (>45°)?	☐	☐
i.	Is the culvert level rather than on a gradient?	☐	☐
j.	Is the culvert made from a rough material?	☐	☐
k.	Is the maximum darting distance of the fish greater than the length of the culvert?	☐	☐

Is the structure a barrier to fish migration? ☐ definitely ☐ probably ☐ possibly ☐ unlikely

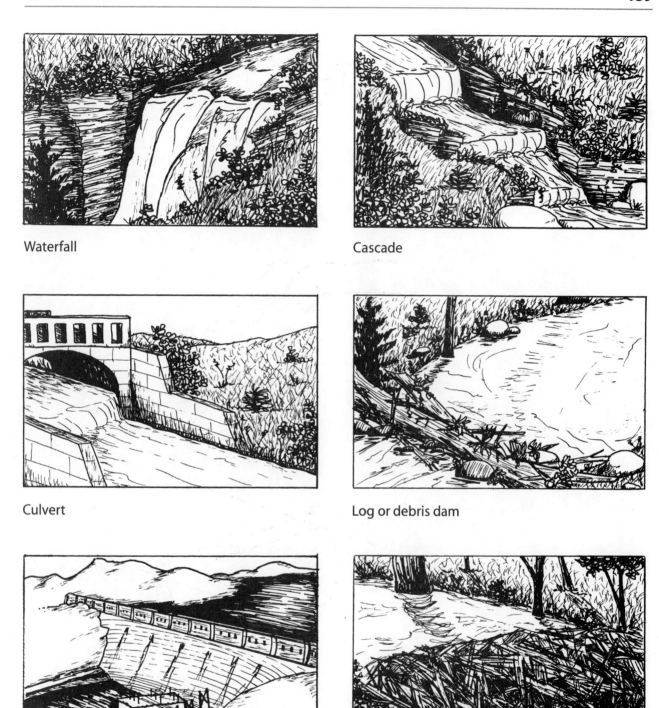

Waterfall

Cascade

Culvert

Log or debris dam

Artificial (constructed) dam

Beaver dam

Figure 13.1   Examples of natural barriers and small artificial barriers.

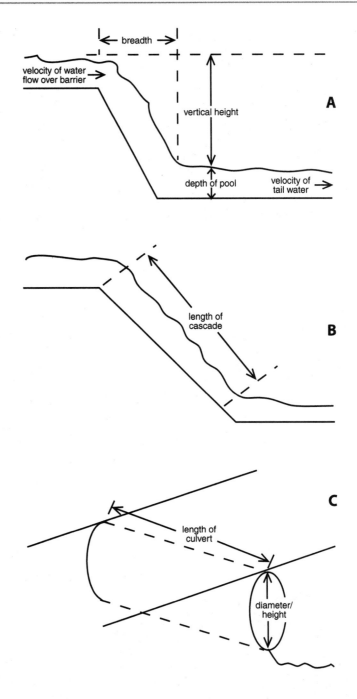

Figure 13.2   Dimensions and hydraulic features to be measured for falls (A), cascades (B), and culverts (C).

- Depth of pool in front of barrier.

- Velocity of water flow over the barrier; measure at a point just before the water begins to fall over the structure.

- Velocity of the tail water; measure where water begins to flow out of the plunge pool.

- Cascade length: measure as shown in Figure 13.2 or compute the length as the square root of the sum of the height of the barrier squared and the breadth of the water flow squared. This formula derives cascade length as the hypotenuse (c) of a triangle with the height (a) and breadth (b) of the barrier as its sides:

$$c = (a^2 + b^2)^{1/2}.$$

- **Characterize the fish.** Identify which fish species could have movements blocked by the potential barrier. Information on the average size and the maximum jumping height of the migrating fish must be available to complete this section. Table 13.1 provides maximum jumping heights for some common salmonid fishes. Maximum jumping height (h) can be estimated for other species using the formula of Reiser and Peacock (1985):

$$h = v^2/2g;$$

  h = maximum jumping height;
  v = fish darting speed (see below);
  g = acceleration due to gravity (9.8 m/s²).

  Fish darting speed (v) is the maximum swimming speed attained in a 2–3 s period. It is estimated as 8–12 times average fish length (l). The healthier the fish, the higher the number. Use 9 unless expert knowledge of the status or age of the fish suggests a different value. If the standard darting speed value is used, the maximum jumping height becomes

$$h = (9l)^2/2g.$$

  See Box 13.2 for an example calculation.

- **Summarize results.** Answer each of the questions listed in Box 13.3 that pertain to the potential barrier. These questions are on the sample field form, Box 13.1, in abbreviated form. Review the answers to all relevant questions. If any of the first four ques-

Table 13.1   Maximum jumping heights of some migratory fishes as reported in Reiser and Peacock (1985).

Species	Maximum jumping height (m)
Oncorhynchus tshawytscha chinook salmon	2.4
Oncorhynchus kisutch coho salmon	2.2
Oncorhynchus nerka sockeye salmon	2.1
Oncorhynchus gorbuscha pink salmon	1.2
Oncorhynchus keta chum salmon	1.2
Salmo salar Atlantic salmon	3.3
Oncorhynchus mykiss steelhead	3.3
Salmo trutta brown trout	0.8
Oncorhynchus clarki cutthroat trout	0.8
Thymallus arcticus grayling	0.9

Box 13.2   Example fish jumping height calculation.

Calculation of jumping height (h) for a fish whose length (l) is 0.35 m.

$$h = v^2/2\,g$$

where v is estimated as 8 to 12 times the fish length, depending on the health of the fish. For this example, with no knowledge of the health of the specific fish in question, assume its maximum swimming speed is 9 times its body length per second.

$$h = (9l)^2/2\,g$$
$$= (9 \times 0.35)^2/2(9.8)$$
$$= 0.51 \text{ m}$$

tions (a–d) were answered "no," the structure poses a definite barrier to fish migration. If one or more of questions e–k were answered "no," the structure is a possible barrier to fish migration. Consider which question(s) were answered "no" and weigh their relative importance to the specific structure and fish in the stream reach. If all of the above questions were answered "yes," then the structure is an unlikely barrier to fish migration.

13.2.4 Notes

The technique outlined above requires some judgements that can heavily influence final conclusions. Barrier assessment accuracy and confidence depends on the analyst's knowledge about the biology of the fish being studied. Keep in mind that different species of fish will react differently to specific environmental conditions. In question e of Box 13.3, for example, turbulent versus laminar flow can be difficult to determine, and there are no absolute rules on when water is calm enough to allow normal fish movement. However, previous experience with the fish species will aid assessment of fish response to turbulent water. Similarly, in questions f and g, it may be time consuming if not impossible to determine precisely where swimming performance significantly declines, or the exact oxygen level that will limit swimming power. Consequently, knowledge of the particular limitations of the fish species and stream setting can guide judgments on whether the structure is a barrier.

13.3   Assessing Large Artificial Dams

13.3.1 Rationale

Large artificial dams usually block fish migrations because of their size and construction; however, many dams that prohibit fish move-

Box 13.3   Questions used to determine if a structure is a barrier to fish migration.

a. Is the maximum jumping height of the fish higher than the height of the structure?
b. Is the darting speed of the fish faster than the velocity of the water flow over the structure?
c. Is the darting speed of the fish faster than the velocity of the tail water?
d. Is the depth of the plunge pool either greater than 1.25 times the height of the barrier or more than 2.5 m deep?
e. Does the plunge pool water return from turbulent to laminar flow within one-third the height of the structure out from the base of the structure? One third the height of the structure is a rough estimate given to help you judge if the water is calm enough to allow the fish to reach maximum jumping height.
f. For anadromous fish, is the barrier less than halfway along the travel distance of the fish between the mouth of the river and the spawning ground? For catadromous fish, is the barrier less than halfway from the headwaters to the mouth of the river? Again, half the distance is a rough estimate. The closer a fish gets to its spawning ground, the lower its maximum jumping height is likely to be.
g. Are other environmental factors that could affect fish jumping abilities, such as temperature or oxygen, within the ideal range required by the migrating fish?

For cascades

h. Does the cascade have a steep gradient (>1) rather than a low gradient (<1)? A slope of 1 is a rough estimate. A low gradient is harder to jump over, because the depth of the cascade is harder to clear. However, a low gradient cascade may be swum over if the length of the cascade is not very long and the water flow is not faster than the fish.

For culverts

i. Is the culvert level rather than on a gradient? Culverts on a gradient have faster water velocity.
j. Is the culvert made from a rough material (e.g., not metal) that will slow water flow?
k. Is the maximum darting distance of the fish (= darting speed of fish per second $\times$ 2–3 seconds) greater than the length of the culvert?

ment have fishways or fish passage facilities, such as a fish ladders or locks. The barrier potential of the dam then depends on the ability of the fish to use the fishway successfully. The effectiveness of fishways is highly variable. Many migrating fishes are sensitive to hydraulic changes in and near the fishway, so the presence of a fishway does not ensure that fish migrations are unimpeded (Bell 1986). Fishways must be carefully constructed to promote fish passage; the approach to a fishway is equally important. Changes in hydrology or topography of a fishway approach may discourage fish from getting to the vicinity of the fishway. Operators of dams and fishways may have data on whether the facility is used successfully by migrating fish, what fish species use the facility, and what percentage or how many fish successfully pass. In addition to this information, physical attributes can be used to assess fishway effectiveness and identify problems.

13.3.2 Preparation

▶ Contact dam and fishway operators to obtain available data and information.

▶ Acquire maps of the dam site, facility design specifications, and operating or licensing information.

13.3.3 Procedures

■ **Basic description.** Record distance from the mouth of the stream or river to the dam. Obtain a facility design drawing, site map, or aerial photographs to locate the dam and document the site configuration.

■ **Record dimensions.** Follow the technique above (section 13.2) if the dam does not have a fish passage facility. If the dam has a fish passage facility, contact the operators to obtain the following information:

- What is the discharge regime of the facility, both seasonally and daily?

- What fish are targeted by the facility?

- Is the facility used successfully by these fish?

- When do these fish use the facility?

- What percentage or how many of the fish successfully pass?

Dimensions of the dam may vary depending on the daily and seasonal discharge regime. For example, downstream water surface elevation is often dependent on dam discharge rate. Dam dimensions should be estimated based on typical flow conditions when the target species reaches the dam during migration. Assess dimensions during several discharge regimes for dams that have fluctuating discharges or to test the general barrier characteristics. These data can be used to compare the effectiveness of fish passage facilities during different discharge periods. Measure, estimate, and record the following (data are often available from the dam operators):

- height, width, breadth of dam, width of the spillway, and velocity of the tail water (for descriptions of some measurements, see section 13.2.3);

- the type of fishway, upstream and downstream;

- dimensions of the fishway, including gradient, length, velocity, and configuration;

- topography leading into the fishway, including any structures used to corral the fish toward the fishway.

■ **Evaluate the barrier potential.** Barrier status will depend on the data from the fish passage facility. These data should indicate the type and number of fish passing through the facility as well as the time when they pass. Expert knowledge of the fish being studied will aid this evaluation by providing an expectation of migration patterns without the dam. Fish passage data may reveal that the dam acts as a barrier but not all of the time (e.g., fish only pass through the fishway under certain conditions). These data can then be compared with the physical characteristics of the dam and fishway to find common traits of dams where the fishways are not effective.

13.3.4 Notes

The cautionary notes in section 13.2.4 also apply to the large dam technique above. Assessing large dams requires judgements that can heavily influence final conclusions about fish passage effectiveness. Assessment accuracy depends on the analyst's knowledge about the biology of the fish being studied and the design of fishways. Information from dam and fishway operators will be key in any assessment. Although there may not be much information about fish passage for dams and fishways built more than a century ago, a lot is known about passage at newer facilities.

13.4 Assessing Stream Habitat Conditions as Potential Barriers

13.4.1 Rationale

In addition to physical structures, habitat conditions can serve as barriers to fish migration. For example, stream channelization often produces habitat conditions with either very elevated water velocity or broad, shallow channels that limit or block fish movements. Habitat conditions should be quantified to complete a thorough assessment of fish barriers.

13.4.2 Preparation

▶ Develop familiarity with stream habitat conditions, standard measurements, and use of equipment necessary to fill out the data sheet.

▶ Develop thorough knowledge of fish species in the study area.

▶ Obtain a map of the stream, marked in river miles or kilometers. The map should include both the origin of the migrating fish and their final destination.

▶ Acquire measuring tapes and an instrument to measure water velocity (see Chapter 14, Streamflow, for different techniques and equipment). A boat may be needed for large waters.

▶ Duplicate a data recording sheet for field use (sample provided in Box 13.1).

13.4.3 Procedure

■ **Basic description.** Record how far the habitat survey is from the mouth of the stream. Draw a sketch of the stream reach and record prominent natural or constructed (e.g., bridges, roads) features.

■ **Assess water velocities.** Perform the following steps (adapted from Reiser and Peacock 1985; Bell 1986) if elevated water velocity is suspected of restricting fish movements.

- Measure and record representative water velocities through a channel section of stream, and record the length of the stream where water velocities are high.

- Identify which fish could encounter the potential barrier conditions, and determine their average size (total length, l). For the fish of interest, identify cruising swimming speeds (maintained for extended period of time) as 2–4 times l per second. If cruising speed of the fish is greater than the typical water velocities, then water velocity is not likely to pose a barrier to fish movements.

- Identify sustained swimming speeds (maintained for several minutes) as 4–7 times l per second. If sustained swimming speed of the fish is greater than the water velocity, multiply the swimming speed by 5–8 min to get the total distance the fish can travel at that speed. If this distance is longer than the length of the stream section with increased velocity, then the water velocity is not likely to pose a barrier to fish movements.

- Identify darting speeds (maintained for a few seconds) as 8–12 times l per second. If darting speed of the fish is greater than the water velocity, multiply the speed by 2–3 s to get the total distance the fish can travel at that speed. If this distance is longer than the length of the stream section with increased velocity, then the water velocity is not a likely barrier to fish movements.

■ **Assess water depths.** Measure the length of stream and water depths along the thalweg, where low water levels might restrict fish movements. Identify which migratory fish will encounter the potential barrier conditions, estimate their body dimensions, and consider the probable responses to shallow water. Judge if water depths could prohibit swimming or pose conditions strongly avoided by the fish. Use knowledge of these fish to determine if they can pass through the water at available depths.

- **Evaluate the potential barrier conditions.** Make a final determination of the potential barrier effect of poor habitat conditions. This will often rely on judgements, but use the data on water velocities and depths to justify and support a conclusion.

13.4.4 Notes

Assessing stream habitat conditions as fish migration barriers is not as common as the two techniques described above. However, natural habitat barriers are increasingly common in regions where there is a growing human population. Where flooding is being minimized by stream channelization, the loss of natural meanders increases the water velocity during high flow periods when many fish move for spawning. Dry periods also impact fish passage when water withdrawals substantially reduce streamflows in heavily populated or intense agricultural areas. The habitat assessment technique presented here addresses these problems by specifying measurements that can be used with fish swimming and morphology data, to provide informed judgements about habitat conditions posing migration barriers.

Streamflow

14

Anne S. Gallagher and Nathalie J. Stevenson

14.1 Introduction

14.1.1 Background

Streamflow or discharge is the quantity of water passing through a cross section of a stream channel per unit time. Stream velocity (recorded in m/s) and the cross-sectional area (m²) produce volume per unit time (m³/s). Water velocity or current speed is a component of discharge and is recorded as a rate (m/s) for a point in a stream. While discharge estimates depend on velocity measurements, fish and other stream organisms often respond to water velocity in their immediate vicinity or microhabitat (e.g., Growns and Davis 1994; Hart 1996). Techniques for measuring water velocity can be used for point estimates in stream microhabitats, or in a series of cross-sectional measurements for estimating discharge.

Discharge is a product of the hydrologic cycle; therefore, it varies with topography, geology, climate, season, vegetation, and drainage area. Streams with land surface runoff and tributary inflows tend to have highly variable flow, whereas streams with substantial groundwater input (channel seepage and springs) have more stable flows. Drainage basins with intense human land use (agriculture, urban areas) and little riparian vegetation tend to have streams with highly variable discharge that quickly responds to precipitation; forested basins and streams with heavily vegetated riparian zones typically have more constant streamflow. Headwater streams vary in discharge based on local basin conditions and recent precipitation. Large streams and rivers drain large land areas and tend to have average basin conditions and moderately variable streamflow.

Changes in stream discharge affect water depths, substrate composition, suspended sediment loads, and nutrient and sediment transport. Streamflow directly affects habitat composition, and variability in streamflow largely determines habitat stability. Habitat composition and stability in turn affect the biotic components of a stream, especially fish community composition. Discharge can also affect riparian vegetation, which provides important fish cover and erosion control. Discharge determines the extent of stream channel inundation and the duration of inundation influences riparian soil moisture, soil oxygen concentration, and vegetation composition and distribution (Auble et al. 1994).

14.1.2 Selection of Techniques

Two techniques for determining stream discharge are outlined in this chapter: one involves fieldwork and one uses available streamflow data and applies them to habitat assessment sites. These techniques provide a choice of field or office procedures, as well as a choice of precise, point-in-time discharge estimates or approximations of discharge rates at any time or time period. The first technique is used to measure discharge in the field and includes three ways to measure stream velocity. Measure discharge in the field when precise measurements are needed for other assessment procedures. The second technique relies on extensive stream discharge monitoring data of the U.S. Geological Survey (USGS) and explains how to apply this information to a habitat assessment site. Available discharge data works well for approximating discharges that are defined over time (e.g., annual or monthly means, baseflow levels). In general, the field technique will be most useful for matching discharge to other habitat assessment data, and use of USGS data will be useful for characterizing discharges over time.

14.2 Cross Section Measurement

14.2.1 Rationale

Streamflow or discharge is the volume of water passing through a stream per unit time, so a simple way to estimate discharge is to multiply a cross-sectional area by the average velocity of the water. However, water in a channel flows at different speeds depending on its location. Friction from the streambed and from the air reduces velocity, and velocity of water moving through habitats within streams (e.g., riffles, runs, pools) varies markedly. It is, therefore, necessary to divide a stream cross section into subsections and determine the discharge of each subsection. The total of all the incremental section discharges equals the total stream discharge.

14.2.2 Preparation

▶ Assemble a tape measure or tag line, stakes, and a water velocity measurement device (meter, float and stop watch, or velocity head rod).

▶ Calibrate or test water flowmeter before fieldwork using the instructions specific to each device.

14.2.3 Procedures

■ Stretch a tape measure (small streams) or metal tag line (marked wire line) across the stream, perpendicular to streamflow. Anchor the tape measure between two stakes. The tape measure should be level and taut. Unless discharge across a pool is specifically needed, it is best to measure discharge across a section of smoothly moving water, such as a riffle or run. Measure the width of the stream, from water's edge to water's edge. Divide this distance by 20–25 to set the approximate measurement (depth, velocity) interval. These interval widths do not have to be consistent. Closer intervals should be used for deeper or swifter parts of the channel or where there is a change in topography. Larger intervals can be used in shallow areas or where the depth and flow variability are relatively low. No subsection should contain >5% of the total discharge. Starting at the left bank (looking downstream), record the following for each subsection (see Figure 14.1, also sample field form in Box 14.1):

- distance from the left bank along the tape measure,

- water depth recorded from a measuring rod or flowmeter rod (zero at ends of the transect),

- water velocity (measured in one of several ways outlined below).

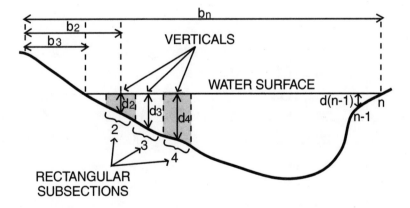

Figure 14.1   Cross section of a stream showing sampling locations for water depth (*d*) and velocity. Note that the interval represented is half the distance between adjacent measurement points except the first, and last interval, to the water edge.

Box 14.1   Discharge Measurement Form.

Assessment site:		
Recorder:		Date and time:
Streamflow condition:		

Distance from left bank endpoint (ft;m)	Water depth (ft;m)	Water velocity (ft/s;m/s)	Cell width (ft;m)	Cell area (ft²;m²)	Cell discharge (ft³/s;m³/s)	Notes
	0	0	–	–	–	water edge
	0	0	–	–	–	water edge
			Sum is the stream width	Sum is the cross section area	Sum is the stream discharge	

Once velocity measurements have been made, calculate the total stream discharge for each subsection according to the equation below or use the field form (Box 14.1) as a computation worksheet.

$$Q_n = d_n \times \left(\frac{b_{n+1} - b_{n-1}}{2} \right) \times v_n$$

Q_n = discharge for subsection n,
d_n = depth at subsection n,
b_n = distance along the tape measure from the initial point on the left bank to point n,
v_n = mean velocity of subsection n.

If any section has >5% of the total discharge (calculated in next step), subdivide that section into smaller incremental widths and take additional measurements. Calculate the total discharge (Q) for the cross section by adding all of the Q_n's to get total stream discharge (Q_{total}).

Choose a water velocity measurement method that best fits the cost limitations and accuracy requirements.

■ **Flowmeter.** Mount the flowmeter probe on a wading rod. Set the water depth on the wading rod; it will automatically set the flowmeter to 0.6 of the water depth (mean velocity for a position). Hold the probe facing into the current. Stand downstream and far enough back to avoid interfering with the flow of water passing the meter. Depending on the flowmeter, wait at least 30 s for the velocity reading to stabilize. See Figure 14.2 for a picture of this method being done with a mechanical flowmeter. Take either one or two meter readings at each location, depending on the water depth, as described below:

- For water depths (d) < 0.75 m, measure velocity once at 0.6 d from the water surface (e.g., if water is 0.5 m deep, measure velocity at 0.3 m from the water surface). A flowmeter wading rod (Figure 14.2) will automatically set the flowmeter to the correct depth.

- For depths >0.75 m, measure velocity twice, at 0.2 d and 0.8 d. Average these two readings to determine the velocity for that cross section. If the water is too deep for a wading rod, lower the current meter to the proper depth on a graduated cable from a boat or bridge-mounted cable winder. If a wading rod is used, set the depth on the rod to 0.33 and 1.33 of the water depth, which will set the meter to 0.2 d and 0.8 d, respectively (e.g., if water is 1 m deep, set the rod to 0.33 m and 1.33 m. The wader rod will set the meter at 0.6 × the set depth, which equals 0.2 m [= 0.2 d] and 0.8 m [= 0.8 d]).

Figure 14.2   Measuring water velocity with a meter (mechanical type) and wading rod.

Velocity Head Rod

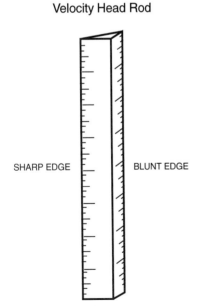

Figure 14.3   Velocity head rod.

- **Velocity head rod.** Hold the velocity head rod (Figure 14.3) in the current so that the sharp edge is facing upstream and record the height (h_0) of the water passing the rod. Pivot the rod around 180° so that the flat side of the rod is facing upstream. This creates an obstruction which causes the height of the water surface to rise on the rod (Figure 14.4). Record the height (h_j) of the water on the flat side. Use Box 14.2 to convert the velocity head ($h_j - h_0$) to mean water velocity for measurement location.

- **Float method.** This technique estimates stream velocity for the whole stream cross section so the field form (Box 14.1) does not apply. Measure and mark two points along the bank at least three channel widths apart. Toss an orange (alternatively use any neutrally buoyant object) in the water and time how long it takes to float between the two points. Repeat this several times and average the travel times to get a mean surface velocity of the water. Multiply this number by a velocity adjustment coefficient to get the mean velocity of the entire cross section. This coefficient varies between 0.8 and 0.95, depending on the roughness of the channel: the smoother the channel, the higher the coefficient. Select a value, however, if in doubt, use 0.85 as the coefficient. Once mean velocity (ft/s, or m/s) is estimated, multiply that times the cross-sectional area (ft^2 or m^2) to compute the stream discharge (m^3/s).

SHARP EDGE   BLUNT EDGE

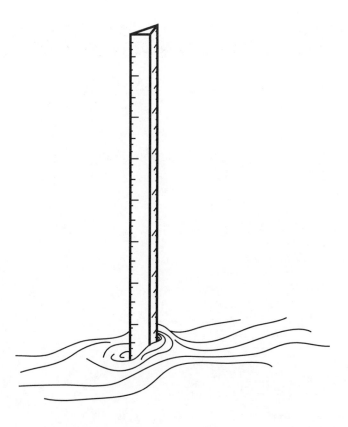

Figure 14.4 Hydraulic head formed on the flat side of the velocity head rod.

14.3   Stream Gauge Data

14.3.1 Rationale

The USGS provides discharge data on a continuous basis as part of their stream-gauging program (Wahl et al. 1995). Data from both active stations and discontinued stations are stored in a computer database that holds mean daily discharge data for nearly 18,500 locations and more than 400,000 station years of records (Wahl et al. 1995). These data are published on a water year basis for each state, which is the 12-month period from October 1 through September 30, and is designated by the calendar year in which it ends. These reports are usually published 6–12 months after the end of the water year so that the data can be reviewed; however, more than half of the currently operating stations make provisional data available as it is collected. Figure 14.5 shows sample output from one of these stations. The raw data are also available.

Box 14.2   Water velocity for different values of change in head.

ft	cm	ft/s	m/s
0.05	1.5	1.79	0.54
0.10	3.1	2.54	0.78
0.15	4.6	3.11	0.95
0.20	6.1	3.59	1.09
0.25	7.6	4.01	1.22
0.30	9.1	4.39	1.34
0.35	10.7	4.74	1.45
0.40	12.1	5.07	1.55
0.45	13.7	5.38	1.64
0.50	15.2	5.67	1.73

PROVISIONAL DATA SUBJECT TO REVISION

03021350-- FRENCH CREEK NR WATTSBURG, PA

Streamflow -- updated Thu Sep 30 06:00 1999 -- download presentation-quality graph

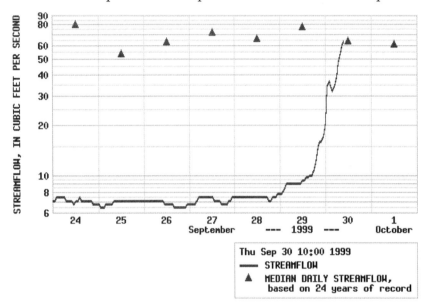

STATION.--03021350 FRENCH CREEK NEAR WATTSBURG, PA

LOCATION.--Lat 42`00'55", long 79`46'58", Erie County, Hydrologic Unit 05010004, on right bank at downstream side of bridge on Tanner Road, 1,200 ft east of State Highway 74, 1.1 mi west of Pennsylvania-New York border, 1.5 mi northeast of Wattsburg, and 2.4 mi above confluence with West Branch French Creek.
DRAINAGE AREA.--92.0 mi².
PERIOD OF RECORD.--October 1974 to current year.
GAGE.--Water-stage recorder. Datum of gage is 1,304.84 ft above sea level (U.S. Army Corps of Engineers bench mark).
REMARKS.--U.S. Army Corps of Engineers satellite telemeter at station.
COOPERATION.--Funding for the operation of this station is provided by the U.S. Army Corps of Engineers, the Pennsylvania Department of Environmental Protection, and the U.S. Geological Survey.

Daily Mean Flow Statistics for 09/30 based on 24 years of record

Figure 14.5   Sample data reported from a gauge station reporting real-time data via the internet.

14.3.2 Preparation

▶ Acquire a computer with Internet access.

14.3.3 Procedures

◼ If the stream under investigation has a USGS gauging station on it, use their data. Access the USGS home page (http://water.usgs.gov/) and select "water data" and then either: real-time water data for continuously reporting stations, or National Water Information System (NWIS) for archived data on all gauging stations.

◼ If the stream under investigation does not have a USGS gauging station, data from a gauged stream can be interpolated to estimate discharge of the ungauged stream. Calculate the drainage area of the ungauged stream (see Chapter 4 for instructions on determining drainage areas). Identify a gauged stream from a drainage basin with similar aspect and elevation. Calculate the drainage area of the gauged stream. Calculate what fraction of the drainage basin from the gauged stream is the drainage basin of the ungauged stream. Assume that discharge of the ungauged stream is the same fraction of discharge from the gauged stream. See Box 14.3 for an example.

Box 14.3   Sample calculation for prorating USGS gauge data to an ungauged habitat assessment site.

Date: 6 December 1997

Habitat assessment site	**Nearby gauged stream site**
	01318500 Hudson River at Hadley, NY
discharge = to be estimated (x)	discharge = 2,032 ft^3/s
drainage area = 1,287 mile^2	drainage area = 1,664 mile^2

$$\frac{\text{drainage area (ungauged)}}{\text{drainage area (gauged)}} = \frac{\text{discharge (ungauged)}}{\text{discharge (gauged)}}$$

$$\frac{1,287}{1,664} = \frac{x}{2,032}$$

$x = 1,572$ ft^3/s is the estimated mean daily discharge on 6 December 1997 at the habitat assessment site.

Note: USGS data are most commonly reported in English units as shown in this example. Convert final result to metric.

Temperature

15

Anne S. Gallagher

15.1 Introduction

15.1.1 Background

Water temperature strongly influences the composition of aquatic communities, and is probably the most commonly recorded habitat attribute. Many fish survive or thrive only within a limited temperature range. Physiological functions are commonly influenced by temperature, some behaviors are linked to temperature, and temperature is closely associated with many life cycle changes. Temperature indirectly influences oxygen solubility, nutrient availability, and the decomposition rate of organic matter; all of which affect the structure and function of biotic communities. As water warms, oxygen and nutrient availability decrease, whereas many physiological and material decomposition rates increase. These temperature-moderated processes can influence the spatial and temporal distribution of fish species and aquatic organisms. Thus, knowledge of aquatic thermal regimes is important for predicting species composition, activity levels, behaviors, and life cycle events.

Water temperature varies with time of day, season, and water depth. The extent of such temperature variations will largely depend on the size and mobility of the water body. Heat gain and loss occurs more rapidly in streams, which are usually shallow and mobile, as compared to lakes, which are more concentrated, stable water masses. Although temperatures are particularly dependent on direct solar radiation, they are also influenced by water velocity, climate, elevation, stream order, amount of streamside vegetation providing shade, water source, temperature and volume of groundwater input, the dimensions of the stream channel, and human impact. Streams are usually not thermally stratified, but large rivers can get much colder as depth increases (Dodge et al. 1981; Simonson et al. 1993).

Large bodies of water have large heat storage capacity. Deep lake waters can store heat, and lakes mix very slowly compared to streams. Lake temperatures near the surface may fluctuate diurnally, and deeper water temperatures may vary seasonally. Lake shape, orientation, and volume (Chapter 16) determine the likelihood of sharp depth-related thermal changes that define a thermocline, the depth where there is a rapid decrease in water temperature of more than 1°C per meter (Wetzel and Likens 1990; Minnesota Department of Natural Resources 1993).

15.1.2 Selection of Techniques

The two techniques described below cover multiple ways of measuring temperature and determining thermal regimes in streams, rivers, and lakes. Point-in-time or single measurements are useful for quick temperature assessments, but thermal variation in some waters (e.g., shallow streams) will limit the utility of the values. Long-term temperature monitoring characterizes the thermal regime and could identify time periods or seasons of key importance. There are many devices for measuring temperature, and specific choices should be determined by management needs, study requirements, time constraints, and budgets. The techniques described here are the ones most commonly used in management investigations.

15.2   Point-in-Time Measurements

15.2.1 Rationale

Single measurements are good for quickly obtaining information that characterizes the general nature of the water temperature regime; for example, coldwater, coolwater, or warmwater habitat. Thermometers and thermistors give immediate results. These small devices can be used by hand in shallow waters or with long-probe meters to assess the vertical temperature profile of a lake. Maximum–minimum thermometers require slightly more work because they must be retrieved after some length of time, usually 24 h, but they provide information on both average temperature and temperature variability.

15.2.2 Preparation

▶   Acquire one or more of the following temperature recording instruments: a hand-held thermometer, a meter with a thermal probe (often part of a meter that records multiple water parameters), a thermistor, or a maximum–minimum thermometer.

▶   Temperature measurement equipment should be calibrated at least once each field season. Depending on the objectives of the study and the importance of the data, equipment should be calibrated more often.

15.2.3 Procedure

■ **Shallow water measurements.** Stream temperature should be measured mid-channel and out of direct sunlight. For broadly representative values, do not measure near any large objects that project above the water surface, as they may elevate readings, or near subsurface springs or seeps, as they may lower readings. Measure temperature in the late afternoon, during the time of maximum daily temperature. If there has been any precipitation within 48 h, this may influence the reading. For a general water temperature measurement, hold thermometer just below the water surface for at least 60 s per reading. To record temperature extremes in shallow habitats, anchor a maximum–minimum thermometer in the stream and leave it for a given time period (generally 24 h). When retrieving the device, record the current temperature, date, and time along with the maximum and minimum measurements shown for the sampling period.

■ **Deep water measurements.** When measuring in water deeper than a few meters (e.g., lakes, reservoirs), use a temperature recording meter with a cable-connected probe. Measure temperature at the surface, at 1 m below the surface, and at 2 m below. Continue measuring in 2-m increments until the lake bottom is reached. A thermocline is being detected when temperature readings drop more than 2°C per 2-m increment, and these water strata should be described in 1-m increments.

■ **Substrate pore measurements.** The water temperature in the interstitial space of substrate can be most easily recorded with a durable thermistor that can penetrate the substrate of a stream or lake. Alternatively, drive a perforated polyvinyl chloride (PVC) tube into the substrate and measure interstitial flow with a hand-held thermometer. Avoid leaving the tube in place between repeat readings, as the interstitial water will equilibrate with the rest of the stream.

15.2.4 Notes

Data from maximum–minimum thermometers can provide a good estimate of average daily temperature. Crisp (1990) computed mean daily temperature calculated from hourly readings over a 24-h period, and compared these means to those estimated with maximum and minimum values: mean = 0.5(maximum + minimum). Both sets of means were very similar (within 0.5°C in 96% of the cases) indicating that the mean of 24 h maximum–minimum values will closely approximate mean daily temperature.

15.3 Temperature Monitoring

15.3.1 Rationale

Measurements recorded over weeks or months result in a complete picture of the thermal regime. Thermal recording devices can be left in the field for a long time, which reduces the number of necessary site visits, but the devices are more costly than regular thermometers.

15.3.2 Preparation

▶ Acquire data loggers (small thermal recording digital devices) with waterproof, submersible cases and appropriate software for available computers. Alternatively, use water quality monitors (e.g., Hydrolab, Yellow Springs Instruments) that are designed to measure several variables, including pH, dissolved oxygen, salinity, and nutrient levels, as well as temperature. The monitors require protective housing while left in the field and cables long enough to reach the habitat being measured. Find a way to anchor data loggers or monitor probes in the water. A perforated PVC pipe tied to an iron bar used as a stake works well in shallow water.

▶ Prior to positioning field instruments, the recording devices should be calibrated against a laboratory thermometer or other reliable equipment.

15.3.3 Procedures

■ **Install and retrieve data loggers.** These small, battery-operated recorders (Figure 15.1) take regular temperature readings over a predetermined period of time. Set the data logger for either the length of time to monitor or the time interval between readings. Put the data logger in a waterproof, submersible case and anchor it in the water so it is completely submerged. Refer to section 15.2.3 above for guidance on placement sites. At the end of the monitoring period, retrieve the data logger and download the data to a computer. Portable computers are useful for immediate inspection of the data.

■ **Using water quality monitors.** The procedure for using water quality monitors is the same as for data loggers, so refer to the preceeding paragraph. They measure variables at regular intervals, and the data can be downloaded to a computer. This technique commands more attention to secure and waterproof field installation because monitors are larger and more vulnerable to damage.

15.3.4 Notes

Basic water quality data, including temperature, can often be obtained from past studies or agency monitoring efforts; refer to Chapter 18 for some sources. By using available data, it is often possible to characterize the annual thermal regime of a stream or lake. In addition, the thermal conditions of a target water body can sometimes be approximated using long-term data sets developed for nearby, similar waters.

Figure 15.1   Thermal data logger commonly used for monitoring temperature in shallow waters.

Lake Morphology

16

Anne S. Gallagher

16.1   Introduction

16.1.1 Background

Lake morphometry refers to the measurement of lake shape and size and comprises surface area, depth, volume, length, width, and shoreline development (shoreline shape). Each of these dimensions is useful for predicting and explaining some biological, chemical, and physical aspects of a lake. For example, the surface area of a lake controls the amount of sunlight a lake can absorb, and this in turn controls the energy available for primary productivity. Also, lake depth determines the illuminated water volume: relatively deep lakes have low rates of photosynthesis per volume. Shoreline development determines the amount of water edge and littoral habitat relative to lake surface area. This morphological property can influence the trophic nature of the lake: the longer the shoreline, the greater the amount of productive shallow-water habitat.

Biologists often compare lakes using only surface area measurements. Cole (1975) reported a direct relationship between surface area and mean lake depth and volume in an analysis of morphometric data from 500 lakes. Larger lakes are usually deeper than smaller ones and have greater volume. However, this relationship does not hold true for small lakes, and notable exceptions exist with large lakes. For example, Lake Chad in central Africa covers more than 16,500 km^2 in surface area, yet its mean depth is a mere 1.5 m, and its volume is only 25 km^3 (Cole 1975). By comparison, Lake Ontario has a similar surface area (19,000 km^2), but its volume is 1,638 km^3 (www.glc.org/docs/greatplace/gplakes.txt). Although lakes can usually be classified by one metric, such as surface area, lake morphometry that includes several dimensions is more useful for characterizing a lake and explaining fisheries attributes.

The size and shape of a lake is often determined by the geological origin of the basin. For example, cirque lakes tend to be shaped like an amphitheater with steep walls because of ice scouring in deep valleys, and meteoric lakes are the size and shape of the meteor that created a depression. The geology of a lake is important not only because it can control the size and shape of a lake, but also because it can influence biological characteristics. Some geological phenomena, such as glacial or volcanic activity, are restricted to certain climates, elevations, or geographic areas. Lakes of a given origin may only be found in some physical locations and lakes clustered in these areas will tend to have a similar origin, age, and colonization pattern. The origin of a lake can control lake substrates and water chemistry. For instance, volcanic lakes tend to have high pH because the lava forming the lake bed is alkaline, whereas lakes formed by erosional processes (e.g., fluvial lakes) will have water chemistry that reflects local rock and soil composition. Finally, lake origin can also affect water flow through a lake or the exchange rate of the water mass.

16.1.2 Selection of Techniques

The techniques described in this chapter provide a set of criteria for comparing morphological and physical features of lakes. These techniques require little fieldwork; however, because they rely largely on information from maps, the accuracy of the assessment depends on accurate and current maps. Three procedures for using map information span a range of technologies. The most accurate procedure involves using geographic information systems (GIS), but it is more expensive and more training-intensive than the two alternative procedures. The overlay technique is the simplest, least expensive method, but it can have a significant margin of error. An intermediate approach requires the use of a polar planimeter. The selection of a technique will depend on available technology and the required accuracy of the final results.

16.2 Lake Dimensions

16.2.1 Rationale

The size and shape of a lake provide the most basic aquatic habitat measures. Measurement of lake dimensions creates a framework for understanding lake processes and a means for comparing attributes among lakes. The technique described here involves using either GIS or two alternative measuring devices. Geographic information systems should be used when available, but the alternative measuring devices are often acceptable and do not require special training.

16.2.2 Preparation

▶ Acquire U.S. Geological Survey (USGS) topographic maps at 1:24,000 scale (preferred, or use 100,000 scale) and a lake bathymetric map with contour lines of equal depth. If a bathymetric map is not available, the information can be obtained from field depth measurements. Lind (1974) provides details for constructing a bathymetric map. Gubala et al. (1994) described a more advanced technique of constructing a high-resolution bathymetric map using GIS framework by linking a depth sounder to a digital global positioning system unit.

▶ Gain access to a GIS unit with a digitizer, software, and a trained technician. Alternatively, obtain a polar planimeter or a 100 dot-per-square-inch transparent overlay with a map measurer (Figure 16.1) and ruler.

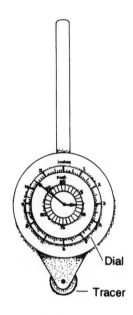

Figure 16.1 Diagram of a map measurer.

16.2.3 Procedures

■ **Lake surface area.** Lake surface area is defined as the surface water area, excluding islands. Measure lake surface area in one of three ways.

1. Digitize the outline of the map using GIS, which calculates the area estimate.

2. Outline the mapped lake with a polar planimeter. A polar planimeter calculates the area of any plane from the movements of a tracer point along a line enclosing a lake. Place the planimeter in a position on the map that allows the tracer point to be moved on the mapped edge of the lake. Record the vernier units (zero at start) on the planimeter once the tracer point encircles the lake. Convert the vernier units to an area measurement based on the scale of the map and conversion units that came with the planimeter.

3. A 100 dot-per-square-inch transparent overlay can be used to estimate lake area. Place the grid transparency over the lake. Count the number of dots falling within the shore boundary line and one-half of the number of dots falling on the boundary line. Check Table 16.1 for the correct conversion factor, based on the map scale in the legend. Multiply the total number of dots counted by this conversion factor to obtain the surface area of the lake in square kilometers.

■ **Basic lake dimensions.** Lake length is the longest straight line that can be drawn across the lake, from shore point to the furthest shore point. Measure this distance using a ruler and convert it to kilometers (refer to the map legend). Lake width is calculated by dividing the lake area by its length. Lake perimeter can be measured two ways: (1) use GIS as described above and

Table 16.1   Conversion factors for 100 dot-per-square-inch transparent overlay grid. Count the number of dots falling within the boundary line of the lake and one-half of the number of dots falling on the boundary line. Convert the number of dots into lake area using the scale of the map.

Scale of map	Distance conversion	Per dot area conversion
1:24,000	1.6 in = 1 km	0.003889 km²
1:100,000	0.3937 in = 1 km	0.06423 km²
All other	x in = 1 km	$0.009956/x^2$

request the perimeter of the lake or length of the shoreline vector, or (2) measure the lake perimeter with a map measurer. A map measurer works by rolling the edge of the measurer along the outline of the lake to record the actual distance traveled. Convert the map measurer reading to kilometers using the map legend and the scale on the measurer. The mean depth of the lake is determined by dividing the volume of the lake (procedure below) by its surface area (procedure above).

■ **Lake shape.** An index of shape or shoreline development is a comparative value that relates the length of the lake perimeter to the circumference of a circle with the same area as the lake. For lakes that are nearly circular, this number approaches 1; elongate lakes or lakes with irregular shorelines have much higher values. Once the lake perimeter and area values are obtained as described above, calculate the shoreline development index with the following equation:

$$\text{Shoreline development index} = \frac{P}{2(A\pi)^{1/2}}$$

P = perimeter of the lake shoreline;
A = surface area of the lake;
π = 3.1416

■ **Lake volume.** The volume of a lake is determined by summing the volume of water at each depth increment defined by the contour lines on a bathymetric map. Measure the surface area, a_i, defined by each depth contour line on the bathymetric map (Figure 16.2), following the directions for surface area estimates above. Include the entire area at depth i and lower, rather than just the area between depth i and depth $i + 1$. For example, if the contour lines on the bathymetric map are marked in intervals of 20 m and the lake is 160 m deep, proceed as follows: measure the area at 0 m depth (total lake surface area); measure the area within the 20-m depth contour line; measure the area within the 40-m depth contour line; and so on through 160 m. If there are two or more areas enclosed by a contour line of the same depth, measure each area separately and sum the areas to get the total

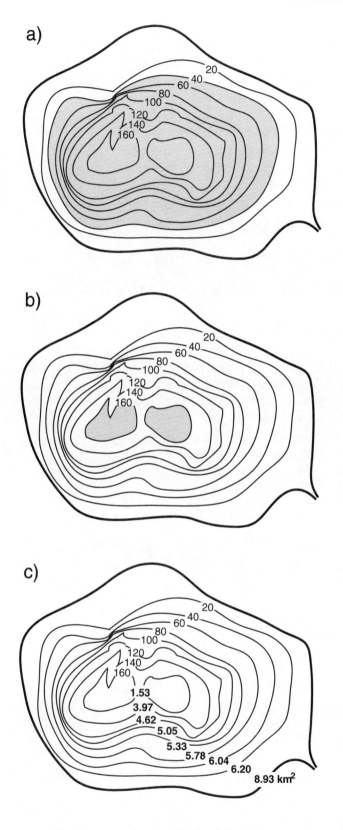

Figure 16.2   Measurement of area at each depth from a bathymetric map: A, area at the 40-m depth interval; B, sum of areas at the 160-m depth interval; C, bathymetric map marked with area at each depth interval.

area for that depth interval. See Figure 16.3 for an illustration and construct a plot like this for the study lake. Mark the left y-axis with the depth corresponding to each contour line. Mark the right y-axis with the surface area, a_i, at each contour depth i (for this example, i runs from 0 to 160 in 20-m increments; a_i = the area at depth i). Mark the distance between depth lines on the cross-sectional view of the lake as in Figure 16.3. Each distance, h_i equals the water depth at depth interval i minus the water depth at depth interval $i + 1$. For example, if the fourth depth line ($i = 4$) is 60 m and the fifth depth line ($i + 1 = 5$) is 80 m, then $h_4 = 20$ m, or 0.02 km. Calculate the total lake volume according to the following equation:

$$\text{Total lake volume} = \Sigma \ (h_i/3) \ [a_i + a_{i+1} + (a_i \cdot a_{i+1})^{\frac{1}{2}}]$$

See Box 16.1 for an example of this computation.

16.2.4 Notes

Divide a lake into sections if a lake map is larger than a 100-dot-per-square-inch transparent overlay or it exceeds the range of a planimeter. Then, measure each section independently and sum the results to obtain total values.

The overlay procedure will yield more precise results by increasing the grid density on the overlay transparency.

If islands are mapped, measure their areas and subtract the total area of the islands from that of the lake total.

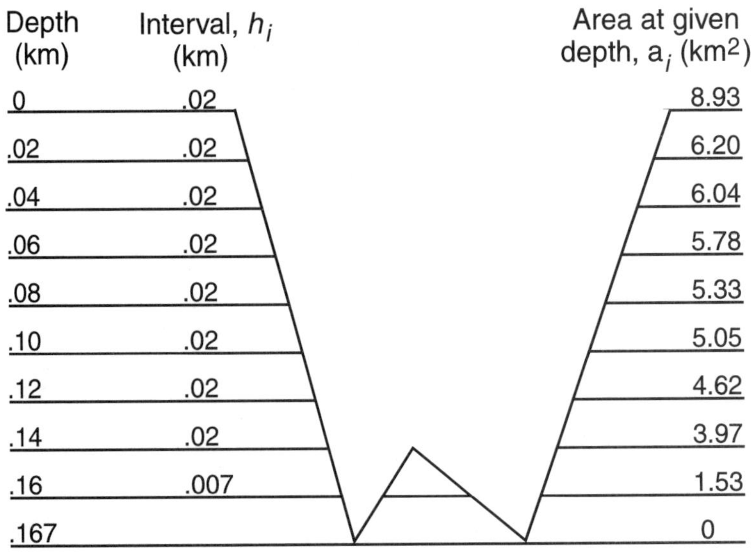

Depth (km)	Interval, h_i (km)	Area at given depth, a_i (km²)
0	.02	8.93
.02	.02	6.20
.04	.02	6.04
.06	.02	5.78
.08	.02	5.33
.10	.02	5.05
.12	.02	4.62
.14	.02	3.97
.16	.007	1.53
.167		0

Figure 16.3   Cross-sectional diagram of lake depth and area corresponding to the illustration in Figure 16.2.

Box 16.1   Example computation of lake volume estimates.

See Figures 16.2 and 16.3 for diagrams showing the source of the data for the following calculations.

Interval i	Depth h_i (km)	Interval area a_i (km²)	Area next interval a_{i+1} (km²)
0	0.02	8.93	6.20
1	0.02	6.20	6.04
2	0.02	6.04	5.78
3	0.02	5.78	5.33
4	0.02	5.33	5.05
5	0.02	5.05	4.62
6	0.02	4.62	3.97
7	0.02	3.97	1.53
8	0.007	1.53	0.00

Using the above figures, follow the equation for total lake volume:

$$\text{Total lake volume} = \Sigma\,(h_i/3)\,[a_i + a_{i+1} + (a_i \cdot a_{i+1})^{\frac{1}{2}}]$$

$$
\begin{aligned}
=\ & 0.02/3 \cdot (8.93 + 6.20 + [8.93 \cdot 6.20]^{\frac{1}{2}}) \\
+\ & 0.02/3 \cdot (6.20 + 6.04 + [6.20 \cdot 6.04]^{\frac{1}{2}}) \\
+\ & 0.02/3 \cdot (6.04 + 5.78 + [6.04 \cdot 5.78]^{\frac{1}{2}}) \\
+\ & 0.02/3 \cdot (5.78 + 5.33 + [5.78 \cdot 5.33]^{\frac{1}{2}}) \\
+\ & 0.02/3 \cdot (5.33 + 5.05 + [5.33 \cdot 5.05]^{\frac{1}{2}}) \\
+\ & 0.02/3 \cdot (5.05 + 4.62 + [5.05 \cdot 4.62]^{\frac{1}{2}}) \\
+\ & 0.02/3 \cdot (4.62 + 3.97 + [4.62 \cdot 3.97]^{\frac{1}{2}}) \\
+\ & 0.02/3 \cdot (3.97 + 1.53 + [3.97 \cdot 1.53]^{\frac{1}{2}}) \\
+\ & 0.007/3 \cdot (1.53 + 0.00 + [1.53 \cdot 0]^{\frac{1}{2}})
\end{aligned}
$$

$$
\begin{aligned}
=\ & 0.150 + 0.122 + 0.118 + 0.111 + 0.104 + 0.097 + 0.086 + 0.053 + 0.004 \\
=\ & 0.845 \text{ km}^3
\end{aligned}
$$

16.3   Lake Geology

16.3.1   Rationale

Lake geology describes two features—lake genesis and lake physiography—that can determine many physical, chemical, and biological attributes of the water body. Lake genesis is the geological origin or physical action that created the lake. Lakes can be formed by long-term geological processes (e.g., glacial or tectonic activity), short-term physical activity (e.g., landslides), or anthropogenic activity (e.g., artificial dams). Lake physiography is the physical location of the lake, which is described by its latitude, longitude, and elevation.

16.3.2 Preparation

▶ Acquire a USGS topographic map of the lake (scale 1:24,000 for smaller lakes, 1:100,000 for larger lakes). This map can be supplemented with other areas maps and aerial photographs.

▶ Determine if a water level gauging facility is located on the lake or obtain supplies to establish a water level benchmark. A boat may be needed to obtain readings from a water level gauge or benchmark depending on locations.

16.3.3 Procedures

■ **Lake formation.** Determine the geological or physical origin of the lake, based on knowledge of the geology of the surrounding area. Table 16.2 shows lake classification based on formation processes. The same force is often responsible for all natural lakes in a given geographic area, so if several lakes are being examined in one area, they usually will have been formed by the same process.

Table 16.2   Classification of lake formation processes.

Class	Formation process	Common associations
Glacial	Movement of glaciers	High latitudes and elevations
Cirque lakes	Ice scouring of steep valley forming a depression Tend to be shaped like an amphitheater with steep walls except at the outlet	
Moraine lakes	Deposition of debris and drift from glacier scouring	
Kettle lake	Depression following the melting of buried ice	
Fluviatile	River activity	Large streams, rivers
Volcanic	Dam or depression formed by lava flow or collapse of a volcano or lava	Areas of volcanic activity
Tectonic	Uplift of earth's surface or drop of earth's crust	Fault lines and areas
Wind	Deposits of sand or silt carried by wind	
Solution	Dissolution of soluble, carbonate rock by percolating water	Carbonate rock areas
Shoreline	Wave action of a larger water body	Large lake or sea margins
Landslide	Mass movement of soil, rock, and debris	
Organic	Buildup of peat and other organic matter	
Meteoric	Meteor impact	
Beaver	Beaver dam construction	On or near streams
Anthropogenic	Artificial (constructed) dams	

- **Identify lake location.** See Chapter 5 for techniques to identify lake location.

- **Measure lake level.** Monitor lake level fluctuations by recording the height of the water in relation to a water level gauge or benchmark. Lake levels are often available from stage or lake level recording facilities. When such a facility does not exist, a benchmark can be established by one of three procedures.

    1. Permanently mount a gauge (ruled plate or metal strip) on an existing solid structure such as a dam or bridge support. The gauge should be marked in depth increments of interest for the habitat assessment. Ensure that the gauge extends lower than the anticipated low water mark and higher than the expected high water mark.

    2. A rock face on the lake shoreline or in the lake (such as on a permanent island) can serve as a fixed point for lake level measurements. In these cases, paint a small circle on the rock about one meter above the high water mark. Drill a hole several centimeters deep in the center of the circle. Measure water level from the height of the hole down to the surface of the water.

    3. A large tree can be used in place of a rock face, and the same procedure can establish a fixed point for lake level measurements. Trees are, however, less dependable over long periods of time than bedrock and concrete dams.

Water Transparency

17

Mark B. Bain and Kristin M. Hynd

17.1 Introduction

17.1.1 Background

Fisheries biologists almost always document some aspect of water clarity in assessments of lake and stream habitats, although their reasons for measuring water clarity are highly diverse. For streams, biologists are most often measuring the sediment load suspended in the water. For lakes, measuring algal production in surface waters and measuring the depth of light penetration to define the extent of the littoral zone are the usual goals. All common techniques record some property of light transmission in water (i.e., the optical properties).

Sediments entering a stream can remain in the water column as suspended sediments or settle onto the bottom as deposited sediments. All streams contain some suspended and deposited sediments naturally. Several factors may increase the sediment load of a water body to a level that is detrimental to biological communities. The primary sources of inorganic sediment in streams are the erosion of uplands, lateral movement of channels into streambanks, and downcutting of streambeds (Waters 1995). Excessive sedimentation usually occurs as the result of human activity, including but not limited to agriculture, logging, mining, and urban development. Suspended sediments are fine particles, primarily clays, silts, and fine sands, that require only low velocities and minor turbulence to remain suspended (Allan 1995). Dissolved sediments have entered into solution, and these will not settle out of the water even if allowed to stand still. The techniques discussed in this chapter vary in their ability to distinguish between suspended and dissolved material, but either may be adequate for habitat assessment purposes.

17.1.2 Selection of Techniques

The two techniques described below can precisely record light transmission in lake water, and often identify the type of material involved. The technique should be chosen based on the availability of equipment and assessment information needs. The most common technique uses a Secchi disk: a 20-cm circular plate painted with a standard pattern that is lowered into water until it disappears from view and then raised until it reappears (Orth 1983). This is one of the simplest techniques for measuring transparency, but it is prone to variable accuracy and is a measurement device that is affected by anything that reduces light transmission in water including surface water reflection. This technique is not described in detail because of its limitations, but the widespread measurement of Secchi transparency has been useful in monitoring lake and reservoir water conditions.

17.2 Turbidity

17.2.1 Rationale

Turbidity is a measure of the extent to which light penetration in water is reduced from suspended solids (Armantrout 1998). Turbidity (also nephelometry, detecting transmitted light with instruments) has a history of use (e.g., Tebo 1955) as a rapid and indirect measure of suspended sediments. The terms turbidity and suspended solids are often used interchangeably. Turbidity is easy to measure rapidly and produces more accurate light transmission readings than can be obtained with a Secchi disk. Also, the U.S. Environmental Protection Agency (1986) quality criteria for water specifies that suspended solids and turbidity should not be elevated to a level where the depth limit for photosynthetic activity (e.g., in lakes) is reduced by more than 10% of the seasonal norm. Turbidity measurements are therefore consistent with many state and federal water quality regulatory programs.

Suspended sediment is the major contributor to turbidity, however, other materials also contribute to the reduction of transmitted light. Turbidity may be caused by pollution derived color, optically active dissolved and colloidal material, organic detritus and pollution, plankton, and other microscopic organisms. Even in the absence of these confounding factors, turbidity measurements can be influenced by suspended sediment grain size, composition, density, and indices of refraction (Earhart 1984). Therefore, when using turbidity as a general measure of water clarity, it should be understood that all factors affecting light transmission are captured in the readings.

17.2.2 Preparation

▶ Acquire a field nephelometric turbidity meter. These meters measure light transmission through sample cuvettes of standard and sample water. They are fairly inexpensive (US$600–900), small, and available in rugged field models.

▶ Prepare data recording sheets.

17.2.3 Procedures

■ **Samples and meter readings.** Obtain a surface water sample, agitate the sample, and fill a meter cuvette. Follow meter instructions to obtain light transmission values in nephelometric turbidity units (NTU). Repeat for three to five samples collected at representative and well-spaced locations in the habitat being assessed. Record each single measurement; data can be reported as a mean or as a range of values.

17.2.4 Notes

This technique is simple and straightforward to conduct. Results can be obtained in the field and data are available immediately. The level of resolution is sufficient to meet most management evaluation needs. As with all physicochemical water measurements, the values obtained reflect conditions at the time of sampling. Although NTU readings will be accurate for the samples processed, the cause of turbidity will not always be evident.

In many field investigations, biologists have extended the meaning of turbidity readings by developing regression equations relating NTU values to suspended solid concentrations (mg/L). This practice may work well under very limited time periods and water conditions (Kunkle and Comer 1971); however, a consistent direct relationship between turbidity and the weight of inorganic sediments per volume of water is unlikely to be valid, because optical properties of water are not fully determined by the mass of solids in water (Earhart 1984).

17.3 Total Suspended Solids

17.3.1 Rationale

Any measure of water transparency captures effects of a variety of suspended and dissolved materials. Suspended sediments are fine particles kept in suspension by turbulence. Dissolved material is in solution, and will not settle out of the water. Dissolved substances may color water and otherwise alter transparency, but dissolved solids are routinely measured by specific conductance (see Chapter 18, Interpreting Chemical Data). A technique that separates the water transparency effects of suspended and dissolved material, and quantifies these components, would be an advancement over nephelometric turbidity meters.

A technique for specifically measuring total suspended solids (TSS in mg/L) is described here (also see APHA 1998). It has been used for many years (e.g., Cline et al. 1982), often under the older name of total nonfilterable residue (as in APHA 1980). Habitat assessments are often aimed at inorganic sediment inputs to lakes and streams; however, suspended solids may contain substantial organic matter. The TSS technique can be expanded to distinguish between organic and inorganic suspended solids (Lemly 1982). Measuring total suspended solids is done in a laboratory, but much of the sample processing can be done in the field.

17.3.2 Preparation

▶ Acquire field items for initial processing on-site: ruled sample bottles, hand pump and vacuum flask, filter folder and filters (2.0 μm or smaller pore size, standard glass-fiber filter), and storage bags for used filters. Bottles and filter disk bags should be labeled before sampling.

▶ Laboratory processing requires a drying oven (muffle furnace for expanded technique), desiccator, and sensitive balance.

17.3.3 Procedures

■ **Field sampling.** Obtain three to five water samples (select a volume that yields 2.5–200 mg of residue; collect plenty and adjust) spanning the habitat being assessed. Filter each sample in the field with hand vacuum pumps and unbreakable filter funnels so that only the small disks are retained for laboratory work. Water samples or filter disks can be stored for up to 1 week at 4°C for further laboratory processing.

■ **Laboratory processing.** Laboratory processing starts with vacuum filtering a well-mixed water sample through a glass-fiber filter (unless samples were filtered in the field). Determine dry filter weights before using. Following filtration, each filter is dried in an oven at 103–105°C for 1 h and then reweighed. Repeat this step if residue is heavy and possibly not well dried. Total suspended sediments are reported in milligrams (sediment on filter paper) per liter of water (APHA 1998). Calculate results:

mg total solids/L = $([A - B] \times 1000)$/sample volume in mL;

A = weight of filter and dried residue in mg
B = weight of filter in mg

■ **Advanced laboratory processing.** To distinguish between organic and inorganic suspended solids, the glass-fiber filters are placed in a furnace at 550°C (1 h) after the initial filtering, drying, and weighing. At this high temperature organic solids are burned so the loss of mass represents the mass of organic sediments. When using the expanded technique, report results for organic suspended solids, inorganic suspended solids, and total suspended solids in mg/L.

17.3.4 Notes

Although TSS analyses are much more complicated and time consuming than using a turbidity meter, this technique provides accurate data on material in lake and stream waters. The types of materials contributing to water turbidity are identified, and sources will often be evident from this information. Details of the analyses and further methodology recommendations are described in APHA (1998) and Hach Company (1992).

The TSS technique could be used in combination with the rapid, meter-based techniques for turbidity and specific conductance (for dissolved solids, see Chapter 18) to obtain a complete information set on suspended and dissolved material, and their effect on overall water clarity. As a guide for interpretation of TSS data, the middle 50% of U.S. streams and rivers range from 18 to 193 mg/L in total suspended solids (Smith et al. 1987).

Interpreting Chemical Data

18

Mark B. Bain

18.1 Introduction

The chemical and material composition of water influences the species composition and abundance of fish. More than a third (36%, U.S. Environmental Protection Agency 1997) of U.S. streams and rivers do not support intended uses because of water quality degradation. The leading causes of impairment are excessive levels of bacteria, sediment, nutrients, and oxygen-depleting substances from agricultural runoff, municipal point source pollution, and habitat alterations (e.g., dams, riparian zone modification). For lentic waters, the U.S. Environmental Protection Agency (1997) reports that more than a third (37%) of ponds, reservoirs, and lakes (excluding the Great Lakes) do not support intended uses because of excessive levels of nutrients, sediment, and oxygen-depleting substances caused by agricultural runoff, municipal point source pollution, and urban runoff. This chapter focuses on the most common physical and chemical data that can be used to assess the quality of water. Other chapters cover related attributes such as temperature (see Chapter 15, Temperature) and sediments (Chapter 17, Water Transparency).

The chemical and material composition of surface water in lakes, rivers, and streams can be organized into five basic components (Figure 18.1): dissolved gases, dissolved inorganic ions and compounds, particulate inorganic compounds, dissolved organic compounds, and particulate organic material. The gases include dissolved oxygen, which is essential for aquatic life and is often affected by land runoff and organic pollution. Dissolved inorganic ion concentrations (minerals), are often measured and reported in habitat assessments because the values for a set of related measurements (pH, hardness, alkalinity, total dissolved solids, and specific conductance) are indicative of biological productivity and vulnerability to

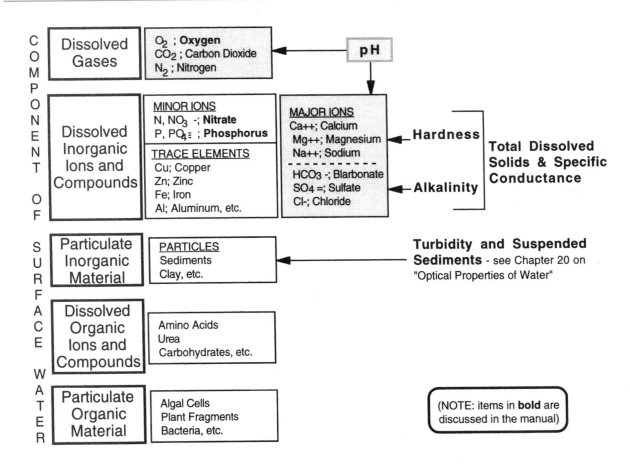

Figure 18.1   Organization of the major components of surface water.

acidification. Nutrients, or minor ions in terms of concentrations, are measured to determine primary productivity and evidence of eutrophication. Finally, particulate (nondissolved) inorganic material is a measure of sedimentation, a major form of habitat degradation.

This chapter is designed to assist fisheries biologists obtain water quality data, and interpret the data for commonly available parameters. Most habitat assessment methods include the use of water quality data. Data on metals, pesticides, herbicides, and other contaminants are beyond the scope of fisheries habitat investigations, and the analysis and interpretation of those data are complex and often controversial. Similarly, biological contamination, such as elevated bacteria concentrations, is not covered in this manual because it is largely a topic of public health (i.e., water consumption and contact).

18.2   Sources of Water Quality Data

18.2.1   Field Sampling and Laboratory Processing

Procedures for sampling and analyzing water are well established and documented. Many state, provincial, and federal agencies have standardized procedures (e.g., U.S. Environmental Protection

Agency 1982, 1983; U.S. Geological Survey 1982; Pritt and Raese 1992; Fishman et al. 1994; Maloney et al. 1994), and are easily obtained (National Environmental Information Service 1997). Commercial water testing companies routinely adhere to the standards and practices specified by the U.S. Environmental Protection Agency (USEPA). Some professional and scientific organizations (American Water Works Association, Water Environment Federation) have maintained recommended methods for sampling and analysis, and these have been in place for decades (e.g., APHA 1980, 1998, and other periodic versions). Some excellent and easy-to-understand independent reference books and manuals (e.g., Lind 1974) on water quality analysis can be purchased. In addition, field and laboratory kits for many water quality parameters are widely available and frequently used in habitat analyses. These kits have well-explained procedures, sampling supplies, and prepackaged reagents. Prepacked reagents and detailed procedures are also available (e.g., Hach Company 1992) for full-precision laboratory analyses.

There is no need to repeat the techniques on water sampling and analysis in this manual with such extensive information already available in several forms; however, some guidance is presented below on how to obtain water quality data for aquatic habitats or adjacent waters, and later criteria are presented (section 18.3) for interpreting water quality data. Keep in mind that standard techniques may already be defined for an agency or a closely related agency in the same level of government. Finally, water quality parameters change rapidly, often from day to day, and with changes in watershed activities, season, time of day, hydrology, and streamflow. More than a single day of sampling is needed to make inferences about water quality for any particular aquatic habitat.

18.2.2 Established Databases

Many state, provincial, and federal agencies maintain large and long-term databases of water quality measurements. Water quality databases will provide more information than could be collected in typical agency habitat surveys because the period of record is usually many years. These databases should be consulted for habitat assessments even when new data are collected so that inferences on water quality can be made from a long-term perspective (explained in section 18.4).

The USEPA maintains a very large water quality database called STORET (Box 18.1) that is the same database used by state water and environmental management agencies. The data in the STORET system came from a variety of sites where water sampling was completed once or often by numerous agencies and organizations. The STORET data comes with agency codes, station codes, latitude, longitude, hydrologic unit codes, date, time of sampling, and about 900 water parameters. Data are obtained from the STORET system by making a specific query, but the method for data queries changes as the system is improved (see Box 18.1).

Box 18.1   Introduction to the STORET water quality database (edited from the USEPA World Wide Web site: http://www.epa.gov/OWOW/STORET/index.html).

Welcome to STORET, EPA's largest computerized environmental data system.

STORET (short for STOrage and RETrieval) is a repository for water quality, biological, and physical data and is used by state environmental agencies, EPA and other federal agencies, universities, private citizens, and many others.

Obtaining Water Quality Data

Until the Legacy Data Center (LDC) and the STORET Warehouse are web-enabled, please call STORET User Support at 800-424-9067 if you wish to retrieve data from STORET. Before calling, be familiar with the available options and decide how you want your data retrieved.

First, you will need to specify your geographic area of interest. Data can be retrieved

- by state or state and county,
- by Hydrologic Unit Codes (HUC),
- by a latitude and longitude and a distance (radius) from that point, or
- by a polygon with the vertices being latitudes and longitudes.
  NOTE: data cannot be retrieved by river name or site (location) name

Next, you will need to know what data you want and how you want it displayed. Data can be displayed

- by an inventory of all the parameters sampled at each station,
- by a composite of all the parameters sampled in all the stations retrieved, or
- by a list of the raw data at each station for selected or all parameters.

Last, you should decide how you want to receive the data. Data can be sent to you

- in hard copy via mail to your snail mail address,
- electronically via File Transfer Protocol (FTP) to a user-specified site, or
- electronically via email, if the file is small.

STORET User Support will discuss these various options with you before initiating a retrieval. Depending on the data available in STORET, retrievals may be limited to certain dates or to certain waterbody types, such as groundwater, lakes, streams, etc.

There is no charge for the information unless the retrieval is for a large area of interest.

STORET User Support
800-424-9067
8:00 a.m. – 4:00 p.m. Eastern
Monday–Friday

The U.S. Geological Survey (USGS) maintains the WATSTORE (Water Data Storage and Retrieval System, Box 18.2) database of water quantity and water quality values for surface and groundwater. The water quality data are extensive and long term (e.g., covering decades). Unlike the STORET system, the data came largely from USGS investigations and monitoring programs, and the sampling sites usually correspond with stations that periodically or continuously monitor streamflow and lake stage.

Many agency databases can be accessed through the Internet. This trend in distributing water quality data is relatively new, and methods for obtaining the data are developing rapidly. A few computer products are available (e.g., CD-ROM) that contain water quality databases (e.g., Alexander et al. 1996) and data from the STORET and WATSTORE systems, but Internet access will probably replace these products in the near future.

Box 18.2   Introduction to the WATSTORE database (edited from the USGS World Wide Web site listed for WATSTORE).

U.S. Geological Survey

Water Data Storage and Retrieval System (WATSTORE)

This section serves as a guide for retrieving data from the Water Data Storage and Retrieval System (WATSTORE). The WATSTORE consists of several files in which water data are grouped and stored by common characteristics and data-collection frequencies. Files are maintained for the storage of (1) surface water, quality of water, and groundwater data measured daily or more frequently, (2) annual peak values and peaks above a base flow for streamflow stations, (3) chemical analyses for surface- and groundwater sites, (4) geologic and inventory data for ground-water sites, and (5) water use summary data. In addition, an index file of sites for which data are stored in the system is maintained in WATSTORE.

The Water Quality File contains results of more than 1.8 million analyses of water samples collected at over 300,000 sites are stored in the Water Quality File. The samples describe the chemical, physical, biological and radiochemical characteristics of both surface and groundwaters. Some analyses contain data for as many as 185 different parameters. However, the average numbers of parameters per analysis is less than 40.

The World Wide Web address for this WATSTORE is:

http://h2o.er.usgs.gov/public/nawdex/wats/intro.html
or
http://water.usgs.gov/public/nawdex/wats/intro.html

For comments and questions, contact: wgreen@usgs.gov

18.3 Common Water Quality Parameters

18.3.1 Dissolved Oxygen

Table 18.1 Solubility of oxygen in pure water at mean sea level air pressure (Lind 1974).

Temperature (°C)	Dissolved oxygen (mg/L)
0	14.16
1	13.77
2	13.40
3	13.05
4	12.70
5	12.37
6	12.06
7	11.76
8	11.47
9	11.19
10	10.92
11	10.67
12	10.43
13	10.20
14	9.98
15	9.76
16	9.56
17	9.37
18	9.18
19	9.01
20	8.84
21	8.68
22	8.53
23	8.38
24	8.25
25	8.11
26	7.99
27	7.86
28	7.75
29	7.64
30	7.53
31	7.42
32	7.32
33	7.22
34	7.13
35	7.04

Dissolved oxygen (DO) enters water from photosynthesis and the atmosphere, and it is used in respiration (from fish to bacterial breakdown of leaves, wood, animals, etc.). Adequate dissolved oxygen is essential to aquatic biota and historically has been one of the most frequently measured indicators of water quality (Hem 1970). Dissolved oxygen concentration in surface waters varies greatly with temperature because the saturation level for oxygen in water decreases as water temperature increases (Table 18.1). In unpolluted, turbulent waters, the dissolved oxygen concentration depends primarily on water temperature. Depletion of dissolved oxygen in streams is caused by algal and bacterial respiration associated with phytoplankton blooms; discharges from municipal and industrial wastewater treatment facilities; leaks and overflows from sewage lines and septic tanks; stormwater runoff from agricultural and urban land; and decaying vegetation, including aquatic plants from the stream itself and detrital terrestrial vegetation (Smith et al. 1993).

The USEPA (U.S. Environmental Protection Agency 1976, 1986) specifies a minimum dissolved oxygen concentration of 5 mg/L as a quality criterion for maintaining aquatic biota. Many states use a less protective minimum limit of 4 mg/L, and some states specify other values due to regional and seasonal conditions. Using the large USGS and USEPA databases described above, Smith et al. (1987) computed that the middle 50% of U.S. waters range from 8.7 to 10.5 mg/L (median 9.8) dissolved oxygen and therefore have adequate levels of oxygen for fish and other aquatic life. During the 1970s, the trend in dissolved oxygen concentration was fairly stable (Smith et al. 1987; Lettenmaier et al. 1991), and this stability prevailed in the 1980s (Smith et al. 1993). One explanation for the stability is that the investment in point-source pollution controls has kept pace with population increases and economic development (Smith et al. 1993).

The following descriptions could be used to interpret dissolved oxygen values in many water quality databases or in new samples:

Description	DO mg/L
Biotic crisis	≤3
Minimum limit in many states	<4
USEPA minimum limit	5
Adequate for fish	>5
Median of U.S. sites	9.8
Middle 50% U.S. sites	8.7–10.5

It is often informative to compare actual dissolved oxygen levels to the saturation level (Table 18.1) at the same temperature; expressed as percent saturation. When this percentage is low (<80–90%) it is evidence of elevated oxygen use, which is often associated with decomposition of organic matter.

18.3.2 Hydrogen Ion Concentration

Potentia hydrogenii (pH) or hydrogen ion activity is a negative $\log_{10}$ expression of hydrogen ion (H$^+$) concentration in moles per liter; pH = 7 is neutral. Restated, pH = $-\log_{10}$ [H$^+$], where [H$^+$] is the hydrogen ion activity. Pure rainwater has a pH of 5.6 because some CO_2 dissolves in pure water forming a weak solution of carbonic acid. Industrial emissions contribute other compounds (e.g., SO_2) to the atmosphere resulting in precipitation with high hydrogen ion concentration (that is, low pH or acid rain). There is an extensive body of scientific literature on acid effects on aquatic biota that emerged from more than a decade of intense study of the acid precipitation threat to North American waters.

The USEPA (U.S. Environmental Protection Agency 1976, 1986) classifies waters suitable for biota as pH 6.5–9. Severe stress to aquatic life is evident at pH levels below 4 units. Using the large USGS and USEPA water quality databases, Smith et al. (1987) computed that the middle 50% of U.S. waters range in pH from 7.3 to 8.1 (median 7.8) in the 1970s. Through the 1980s, pH levels have been increasing in most U.S. waters, especially in the northeastern states, suggesting a reduction in acidity of precipitation (Lettenmaier et al. 1991). The following descriptions could be used to interpret pH values in water quality databases or for new samples:

Description	pH
Stressed	<4
Suitable for biota	6.5–9.0
Most productive	6.5–8.5
Median for U.S. sites	7.8
Middle 50% U.S. sites	7.3–8.1

18.3.3 Alkalinity

Alkalinity is a measure of negative ion (such as hydroxide [OH$^-$], carbonate [CO$_3^{2-}$], bicarbonate [HCO$_3^-$] and others; Figure 18.1) concentrations expressed in ppm or mg/L $CaCO_3$. The level of alkalinity determines the buffering capacity or ability to neutralize acid (H$^+$ ions), and therefore is important for identifying habitats that are vulnerable to acidification. Well-buffered waters are usually associated with soluble sedimentary rock, especially limestone, and are often productive for fish. Finally, well-buffered waters provide a more stable chemical environment not only because of the acid neutralizing capacity of negative ions, but also because these ions complex with metals and other potentially stressful compounds.

The USEPA (U.S. Environmental Protection Agency 1976, 1986) specifies a minimum alkalinity of 20 mg/L $CaCO_3$ as a quality criteria for maintaining healthy aquatic biota. When waters naturally have alkalinity below 20 mg/L, the level should not be reduced by human actions. Lind (1974) classified waters as poorly, moderately, and well buffered (shown below), and these ranges provide easy categorical descriptors of alkalinity levels. Smith et al. (1987) computed that the middle 50% of U.S. waters range from 42 to 162 mg/L (median 104) alkalinity indicating that most waters are moderately to highly buffered. Through the 1980s, alkalinity levels have been increasing in most U.S. waters, especially in the northeastern states, possibly due to reductions in acidity in precipitation and increases in atmospheric deposition of sulfates (Lettenmaier et al. 1991). The following descriptions could be used to interpret alkalinity values in water quality databases or for new samples:

Description	Alkalinity (mg/L)
Minimum acceptable	20
Poorly buffered	<25
Moderately buffered	25–75
Highly buffered	>75
Median for U.S. Sites	104
Middle 50% U.S. sites	42–162

18.3.4 Hardness

Hardness is a measure of positive ion (primarily Ca^{2+}, and Mg^{2+}; Figure 18.1) concentration expressed as mg/L $CaCO_3$. The term "hardness" originated from the fact that water with high concentrations of positive ions is associated with difficulty in getting lather formation from soap (ions complex organic molecules of soap). Alkalinity and hardness are directly related since each measures differently charged ions of the same dissolved materials. Consequently, alkalinity and hardness usually covary through time and among sites. Moderate to high levels of hardness tend to be associated with soluble sedimentary rock, good fish productivity, and a stable chemical environment. Furthermore, organisms such as mollusks and crayfish need calcium for shells and exoskeleton mass.

The USEPA (U.S. Environmental Protection Agency 1976, 1986) classifies waters from soft to very hard to provide easy categorical descriptors of hardness levels. Using the USGS and USEPA databases, Smith et al. (1987) computed that the middle 50% of U.S. waters range from 27 to 157 mg/L (median 68) in the summed concentration of calcium, magnesium, and sodium, or total hardness, indicating that most waters range from soft to hard. Unlike alkalinity levels, changes in hardness have varied across U.S. waters because the concentration of dissolved materials in water is influenced by many human and natural processes (Smith et al. 1993). The following descriptions could be used to interpret hardness values in water quality databases or for new samples:

Description	mg/L $CaCO_3$
Soft	0–75
Moderately hard	75–150
Hard	150–300
Very hard	>300
Median for U.S. sites	68
Middle 50% U.S. sites	27–157

18.3.5 Total Dissolved Solids

Total dissolved solids (TDS) is a measure of the total concentration of dissolved substances (weight of material left in filtered water after evaporation), and therefore an indirect measure of ion concentration. Total dissolved solids is very easily approximated by specific conductance or conductivity (ability to pass an electric current through water). Pure water has very high resistance to electron flow (high ohms) and conductivity is the inverse: measure of electron flow in μmhos/cm or μS/cm (recent sources use the latter). When TDS is high in limestone outcrop regions, it is usually due to ions of calcium, sulfate, and carbonates. Water is low in TDS and dominated by silica in sand or granite dominated regions. In arid regions, evaporation concentrates sodium and chlorides, raising TDS and conductivity. As described for alkalinity and hardness that measure ion concentrations, dissolved materials tend to be positively correlated with biological productivity, promote stable chemical environments, and indicate a watershed with soluble bedrock.

Specific conductance is one of the most commonly recorded water characteristics because it is easy (insert meter probe in water), fast (immediate reading provided), and often practical (meters are inexpensive, durable, and require minimal care or calibration). Lind (1974) reports that TDS can be estimated as 0.65 times specific conductance (SC). The relation between conductivity and TDS is linear ($TDS = k \cdot SC$) but k varies from 0.55 and 0.75 so a regional relation should be developed for accurate TDS predictions (Allan 1995).

The USEPA (U.S. Environmental Protection Agency 1976, 1986) specifies a maximum TDS of 250 mg/L as a quality criterion for water supplies. Smith et al. (1993) classified waters as having low, medium, and high levels (below) of TDS based on an analysis of the U.S. water quality databases. Through the 1970s and 1980s, TDS levels have been increasing in most U.S. waters, especially in the eastern states, and this trend has been attributed to numerous human activities (Smith et al. 1987; Lettenmaier et al. 1991).

The following descriptions could be used to interpret TDS values in water quality databases or for new samples:

Description	TDS (mg/L)
USEPA maximum for water supply	250
New York state maximum	500
Low concentration	<100
Medium concentration	100–500
High concentration	500–1,000
Very high concentration	>1,000

18.3.6 Nitrate

Nitrate is one of two important nutrients (the other, phosphorus, is described later) that are required by plants and algae for growth. Nitrate levels are elevated by agricultural pollution (fertilizer runoff) and sewage (breakdown of proteins) where nitrate (NO_3) is the end product of oxidation of proteins; the other principal inorganic ions, nitrite and ammonia (NO_2, NH_4^+ ions), are transitory. Automobile exhaust and industrial emissions have significantly elevated nitrate levels in the atmosphere. Artificially high nitrate concentrations in surface waters results in public health concerns about human drinking water and the potential for eutrophication, especially in coastal waters where nitrate is often far more limiting to plant growth than phosphate. Direct effects on fish are not evident until levels are so high (>90 mg/L N; U.S. Environmental Protection Agency 1976, 1986) they are rarely seen even in polluted waters.

A widely applied concentration limit for nitrate (expressed as nitrogen) in water supplies is 10 mg/L (U.S. Environmental Protection Agency 1976, 1986) for public health reasons. These levels are far higher than seen in almost all natural surface waters; forested watersheds yield water with nitrate concentrations one hundredth of this level. Smith et al. (1993) use a nitrate concentration of 1 mg/L N as indicative of agricultural and urban runoff effects. Using the USGS and USEPA water quality databases, Smith et al. (1987) computed that the middle 50% of U.S. waters range in nitrate from 0.20 to 0.89 (median 0.41) mg/L. In the 1970s, nitrate levels in surface waters across North America were rising due to increased runoff of fertilizer from agricultural areas and atmospheric deposition (Smith et al. 1987), but the time trend analysis by Lettenmaier et al. (1991) indicated a mix of factors have been responsible.

The following values could be used to interpret nitrate concentrations in water quality databases or for new samples:

Description	NO_3 mg/L N
Undisturbed stream in a forested basin	0.1
Agriculture and urban influenced	>1
USEPA quality limit	≤10.0
No direct effects on fish	≤90.0
Median for U.S. sites	0.41
Middle 50% U.S. sites	0.20–0.89

18.3.7 Phosphorus

In surface freshwaters, phosphorus (P) occurs largely as phosphate (PO_4) and is the component of water chemistry that limits plant production. Phosphorus is vital to all life for synthesizing adenosine triphosphate (ATP), which is the energy carrier in all cells. It is not abundant in natural systems where it is rapidly used up by living things; however, many human activities greatly increase the availability of phosphorus as phosphate, which accelerates growth of aquatic plants and results in eutrophication. Waste discharge from sewage-treatment and food-processing plants and other industrial facilities is the largest source of phosphate in streams. Nonpoint sources of phosphorus include agricultural and urban runoff and, in certain regions, the runoff and groundwater flow from areas that contain natural deposits of phosphate minerals (Hem 1970).

Problematic algae or plant growth usually does not occur if phosphate concentrations remain under 0.1 ppm or mg/L (Winger 1981) and the U.S. Environmental Protection Agency (1976, 1986) uses this as the quality criterion for flowing waters. For lakes and reservoirs, the U.S. Environmental Protection Agency (1976, 1986) maximum quality limit is 0.5 mg/L. These levels are set to prevent eutrophication and nuisance plant growth. Using the USGS and USEPA water quality databases, Smith et al. (1987) computed that the middle 50% of U.S. waters ranged in phosphorus from 0.6 to 0.29 mg/L (median 0.13) in the 1970s. Smith et al. (1987) and Lettenmaier et al. (1991) also reported that phosphate levels were stable during the 1970s despite substantial increases in fertilizer use during that decade. During the 1980s the decline continued as a result of significant reductions in point-source loads and some reduction in nonpoint-source loads (Smith et al. 1993).

The following descriptions could be used to interpret total phosphorus values in water quality databases or for new samples:

Description	Total P mg/L
Undisturbed stream in a forested basin	0.005–0.05
USEPA quality limit; flowing waters	≤0.1
USEPA quality limit; lentic waters	≤0.5
Median of U.S. sites	0.13
Middle 50% U.S. sites	0.06–0.29

18.4 Summarizing Water Quality Data

Single measurements of most water quality parameters are highly variable due to temperature, season, stream discharge, and recent watershed activities (e.g., forest fires, land clearing, farming practices, construction, etc.). Therefore, inferences about water quality from point measurements taken during habitat assessments will be limited. Single water quality values may be informative when used in the context of a longer time series of data, or in comparison to nearby waters sampled under the same conditions. When using a time series of water quality data, it is recommended that summary statistics be used that are robust for highly variable distributions: nonparametric statistics such as medians and interquartile ranges (25–75%). Many of the water quality criteria provided above were based on median and interquartile values computed from large databases. Another useful data summary technique is to compute the frequency of violations in quality criteria such as those presented in the preceding sections. For example, using a 10-year, 35-value record of total phosphorus, one could compute the number of samples exceeding the USEPA stream quality criteria of 0.10 mg/L P. When 15% of the samples exceed quality criteria, degraded water quality is indicated. That 15% rate might be different for lethal conditions such as dissolved oxygen below 4 mg/L or pH less than 4. Finally, all available data and information should be reviewed for each aquatic habitat before classifying a habitat as degraded.

Trends in Methods for Assessing Freshwater Habitats

Appendix

Mark B. Bain, Thomas C. Hughes, and Kristin K. Arend

Fishery management has traditionally focused on population-level rates and processes. However, in the past two decades fisheries and natural resource agencies have increasingly employed habitat-based approaches for resource inventory and assessment. Habitat is now the basis of many forms of species management, mitigation planning, environmental regulation, and impact assessment. In comparison with fish populations, habitat has the advantages of being relatively stable through time, easily defined in intuitive physical terms, and a tangible resource for negotiations and decision making. However, the validity of habitat-based management rests on accurate definitions and measurements. As habitat management has become established, a wide range of agencies have developed numerous methods.

The American Fisheries Society (AFS), working with the U.S. Fish and Wildlife Service, developed a project to evaluate the array of habitat assessment methods being used by agencies with fishery management responsibilities. The project sought to provide a basis for defining a select set of standard data collection techniques and analytic procedures. This report is part of that effort, and our specific objectives were to

1. Assemble methods in use by state, provincial, federal, and private organizations to assess aquatic habitats in the inland waters of North America;
2. Assess and synthesize the techniques used in these methods; and
3. Summarize the common uses and attributes of established methods.

This appendix previously appeared in Fisheries 24(4): 16–21.

A.1 Methods

Agencies with fishery management activities in North American
state, provincial, and federal governments were surveyed by telephone from the fall of 1995 through the winter of 1996. We identified
initial contact offices using the *National Wildlife Federation Conservation Directory* (1995) and the *American Fisheries Society 1994–1995
Membership Directory*. Typically, the main contact person available to
answer questions was a research biologist or chief of fisheries. In
many agencies, multiple people were responsible for assessing
aquatic habitat. In these cases, we tried to contact all agency personnel knowledgeable about habitat assessment methods. Private con-
sulting companies, chosen from advertisements in *Hydro Review*,
Fisheries, and other sources, also were surveyed. Companies that
advertised fisheries expertise and research in environmental sciences
were emphasized in our survey. We asked all agencies and organizations to provide documentation for their established habitat assessment methods.

All documents received were first reviewed to determine if the
method was within the scope of our study and if the documents
were detailed enough to judge method attributes. We then analyzed
relevant method documents in one of two categories and conducted
a full review of established habitat assessment methods with thorough documentation. A detailed form was used to structure summary information and observations of the method: its purpose,
input and output variables, analytical approach, validity, and use.
We conducted abbreviated reviews using a short version of the review form when the documentation was generalized or sparsely
developed or when the method only somewhat addressed habitat
assessment. The abbreviated review form only summarized information regarding method purpose, nature of habitat assessment,
and use.

We included only fully reviewed methods in the tabulation and
evaluation of common properties and trends in habitat assessment.
While we counted the abbreviated reviews as evidence that some
agencies conduct habitat assessment, we did not attempt to characterize method attributes because the documents lacked substantial
portions of the information available from the fully reviewed methods. Also, the abbreviated methods did not include procedures or
analyses that expanded the range of coverage provided in the fully
reviewed methods.

A.2 Results and Discussion

We contacted biologists and fishery managers in 62 U.S. states and
Canadian provinces. More than half (37) of these government fishery agencies used one or more established habitat assessment methods. Most (27) of these agencies used one or more methods that we
fully reviewed because they were well developed and thoroughly
documented. Many (19) state and provincial fishery agencies con-

ducted habitat assessments as a significant management task, but they used ad hoc (developed at the time of need) methods. A minor portion (6) of the agencies reported that they did not conduct habitat assessments.

We contacted national, regional, and special program offices of 19 federal government agencies with fishery and aquatic resource management responsibilities in Canada, Mexico, and the United States. Most (16) of these agencies used one or more established habitat assessment methods, primarily the methods we fully reviewed. The other agencies used ad hoc procedures or had no established habitat assessment methods.

Most (12 of 15) of the private U.S. and international companies contacted conducted habitat assessments. However, all of these organizations reported that they used various methods depending on the involved government agencies and their requests. All of the methods mentioned by contacts as common and established were methods we had already obtained. Therefore, no further information was provided that would add to our evaluations. One exception was the Rosgen Method (Rosgen 1994) by Wildland Hydrology. The Rosgen Method was included as a fully reviewed method because it was an element of several other methods and was a method repeatedly mentioned by agency contacts as important in their work.

Our agency and organization survey clearly indicated that habitat assessment methods were well established in most fishery and environmental management agencies. Consequently, we believed that various approaches and procedures would be involved because of the range of organizational aims and operating styles. Also, some agencies used several established methods, indicating internal diversity of habitat assessment practices. After our contact survey, we received a large number of method documents, roughly a 1-m high pile of papers. Of these, we identified 52 method documents for review: 38 for a full level and 14 for a more cursory summary.

Of the 38 fully reviewed methods, most (31) targeted habitats in or associated with lotic (running water) systems. However, a significant portion (11) of the methods dealt exclusively with lentic (standing water) systems or these methods assessed all types of inland aquatic habitat. We considered all the methods to be directed at assessment, and almost half (17) specifically addressed long-term monitoring of habitat. More methods were oriented primarily to assessing general aquatic environmental quality (23) than to assessing habitat as part of fishery evaluations and status investigations (15). The reported purpose of the habitat assessment methods varied substantially (summarized in Figure A.1), but the dominant purpose for having an organizational method was to standardize measurement techniques and data. Only two methods aimed to assess instream flow, despite the significance of this fishery management practice. Other common purposes for developing habitat assessment methods were providing support for larger environmental assessment programs, having a tool for quantifying and evaluating habitat, and setting salmonid stocking allocations.

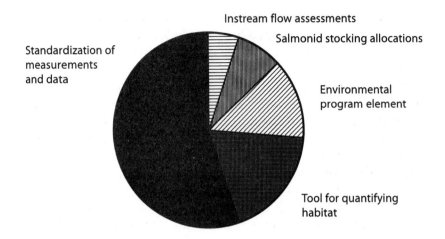

Figure A.1   References for agency methods, depicting the purpose of the 38 aquatic habitat assessment methods reviewed in this study. Statements in the method documentation were used to group the methods into five classes.

The 31 methods aimed at streams and rivers shared many application attributes and limitations. Although most of these methods were developed for the specific jurisdiction of the source agency, most appeared suitable for use throughout much broader geographic scales. In contrast to broad geographic utility, the lotic habitat methods were narrowly focused in terms of habitat applicability. Almost all of the method documents acknowledged the restriction that sampling methods were limited to streams that can be waded. Few methods are truly applicable to large rivers without substantial modification of procedures. Many (10) methods aimed to collect information relevant to all fish species present at an assessment site. Five methods were oriented to the stream community (in the broad sense of multiple taxonomic groups), and eight were aimed at sport fish, largely salmonids. Finally, eight methods had no orientation to a taxonomic group.

The area or site of assessment was highly variable among stream and river habitat methods. Approximately half of the methods varied by application because they depended on site characteristics for identifying sampling area. Six methods specified that study area size (stream length) was to be a multiple of average stream width (10–40 times). This practice is based on the natural frequency of pool and riffle sequences in stream channels. Other methods took an entirely different approach and specified fixed assessment site lengths (40–1,000 m). Consequently, very different approaches are being employed to define how much stream or river habitat needs to be measured. Likewise, fundamental differences existed among methods in terms of how study areas should be located. For almost half of the methods, study areas or sites were selected on the basis of being representative. Random siting of study areas was common, but so was ad hoc site selection. Finally, a few methods employed many sites in order to assess habitat at a watershed or regional scale.

The 31 stream habitat assessment methods included a broad range of variables, and many measures differed in minor ways. Some methods were found to make multiple measurements of similar habitat features. The habitat measures were grouped across methods to summarize the types of data being collected (Table A.1). Physical attributes of stream habitat were heavily emphasized in the 31 methods. All methods included measures of channel size and shape (width, depth, etc.), and almost all methods included water movement (current speed, velocity, discharge, etc.), substrate, cover, and riparian zones (bank and floodplain characteristics). However, stream size (e.g., stream order, drainage area) and watershed attributes (e.g., land use) were often not included, probably because these measures were difficult to obtain without extensive map work. Water quality measurements were included in approximately half the methods (Table A.1) with biological attributes sampled less often. When biological attributes were assessed, fish species composition and relative abundances were most commonly recorded, with macroinvertebrates often included. Fish population estimates were not common, nor were data on fish behaviors (spawning, feeding, etc.) by habitat type.

The 11 methods for assessing lake and reservoir habitats were fairly consistent in capabilities and input measurements. Like the stream methods, most lake habitat methods were intended for the state or province of origin but have broader applicability. The methods were often designed for any type of lake, and we judged most of them to be flexible in application to lentic systems, although survey respondents generally did not specify the way sampling sites were selected for a lake or reservoir. All or nearly all lake methods included measures of lake shape (morphometry), littoral zone features (aquatic vegetation, substrate), water quality, and fish species presence (Table A.1). Assessment methods often included measurements of shoreline or riparian conditions. This shallow-water and shoreline orientation differs from the traditional limnological orientation to deepwater and mid-lake sampling. For example, just 3 of the 11 methods included pelagic zone measurements. Similarly, zooplankton have been the dominant taxa of interest in traditional lake studies, but plankton data were important in only one method. Most methods incorporated relative or catch-per-unit-effort measures of fish abundance, but population structure and fishery variables were not common. Overall, lake habitat assessment methods appeared more consistent than the highly diverse and more numerous stream habitat methods.

Although a variety of computations, statistical calculations, and models were used in the assessment methods, the most common analysis approaches were simple data summaries and calculations of

Table A.1 Attributes measured in the habitat assessment methods for lotic and lentic waters.

Habitat attribute	Number of methods
Lotic waters	31
Physical structure	
Channel dimensions	31
Substrate	29
Water movement	27
Riparian zone	24
Cover	22
Stream size	15
Watershed attributes	8
Water quality	
Temperature	18
Chemistry	14
Biological attributes	
Fish species numbers	16
Fish abundances	11
Invertebrates	10
Fish population size	8
Fish behaviors	6
Fish habitat use	6
Lentic waters	
Physical structure	
Lake morphometry	11
Littoral habitat	9
Submerged vegetation	9
Substrate	9
Riparian zone	7
Pelagic habitat	3
Water quality	
Chemistry	10
Temperature	10
Biological attributes	
Fish species numbers	10
Fish abundances	9
Fish population structure	5
Fishery status	5
Benthos	3
Zooplankton	1

descriptive statistics (Figure A.2). Computations of habitat indices and ratings were used in many methods, and habitat mapping was an important form of analysis. Statistical and dynamic (e.g., hydraulic) models are prominent features of some well-known habitat analysis methods (e.g., Bovee 1982 [IFIM], Binns 1982 [habitat quality index]), but these kinds of analyses were not often built into habitat methods. Most of the habitat assessment methods do not include specialized tools or aids because sophisticated analyses were not common. The primary data analysis tools were database systems (Figure A.3), with frequent use of custom computer programs, reporting forms, and worksheets. Databases and computer programs for data storage were probably undercounted in our summary because some method documents did not address data handling.

Like the measurements and inputs included in the methods, outputs or products of the habitat assessments were highly varied. Outputs were summarized in three groups: numbers and statistics, ratings and indices, and predictions. Numerical summaries and basic descriptive statistics were the most common types of products (Figure A.4) with a focus on habitat attribute values and biota (mostly fish diversity). These reporting numbers reflect data inputs since physical habitat values were most often recorded, and fish species numbers were regularly recorded. Areas by habitat type and statistics on water chemistry were included in some of the method outputs. Composite indices were commonly reported but mainly for habitat quality, whereas respondents reported few indices of biotic health (community composition) and fish population status (Figure A.4). Predictions were an important habitat assessment output (Figure A.4), with fish resource numbers (stocking units, population potential, relative abundances) far more commonly reported than predictions of habitat units.

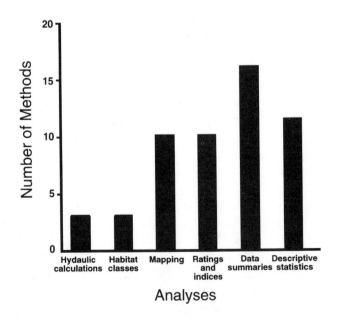

Figure A.2   Approaches used to analyze data collected in the reviewed methods for aquatic habitat assessments.

The reporting format for approximately half of the methods was a database or the enhancement of an existing database. Identifying the presence, location, or amount of habitat by habitat type or class was employed in reporting results from 16 methods. The practice of reporting on available habitats with a numerical description of their characteristics was used in reporting results from more than half (22) of the methods. Overall, analyses often involved simple computations and statistics, which were usually presented in computer (database) and quantitative (habitats with descriptors) form.

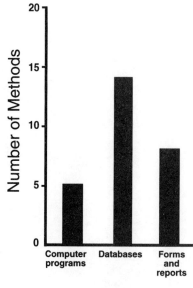

Figure A.3   Tools used to analyze data for the habitat assessment methods.

A.3   Conclusions

Most state, provincial, and federal agencies with fishery management responsibility have been using some type of established method for aquatic habitat assessment. However, a substantial portion (~30%) of the agencies have been relying on ad hoc procedures. The dominant purpose for most methods was to standardize habitat measurements and field sampling techniques. Many of the methods had long lists of habitat attributes that could be measured, and many measurements appeared similar even within single assessment methods. Analysis procedures primarily involved simple computations and statistics, which were usually conducted using a computer database. Databases also were the dominant format for reporting habitat assessment results. Indices, ratings, and predictions of habitat quality are means of making habitat assessment results concise and easily interpreted, but these assessment outputs were not in widespread use. The general trend in habitat assessment aims, various measurements, generally straightforward analyses, and role of databases suggest that many agencies may have first addressed habitat management on an ad hoc basis and later moved to control a proliferation of measurements and field techniques before finally striving to cope with data storage and reporting. If true,

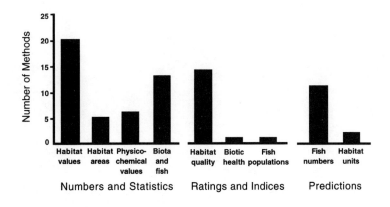

Figure A.4   Types of output information from the aquatic habitat assessment methods that were grouped by major category.

we anticipate that most agencies are in an active period of advancing their efforts, and we should see changes in most methods.

Most fishery biologists probably think of habitat assessment as a stream and river management activity, but we found that one-fourth of the assessment methods were directed at lakes and reservoirs. These lentic habitat methods strongly characterized the littoral zone, shallow-water physical structure, and riparian attributes. Such an orientation contrasts with traditional limnology, which is most often focused on pelagic waters, chemistry, and plankton. For stream habitat assessment, most methods were aimed at physical habitat, but substantial effort also was devoted to water chemistry and the biota. Furthermore, the aims of most stream and lake methods appeared broader than fishery management.

One issue emerged that divided habitat assessment methods into distinct and contrasting groups: sampling design in terms of the size of the area needed and the way study sites should be located. We found specific but inconsistent approaches being used in study design. Determinations of stream site size were being based on principles of geomorphology (e.g., multiples of stream width), field investigator judgment (ad hoc), and past experiences (fixed site sizes). Also, study sites were located on the basis of representativeness, random selection, and investigator judgment. The survey found there were some efforts to expand the scope of habitat assessment by using multiple sites for watershed or regional assessment of habitat resources. Because of the sharply contrasting approaches used in study design, this aspect of habitat assessment warrants investigation to provide managers with guidance on trade-offs associated with the different decisions. Field studies have been reported to identify adequate stream lengths for fish community characterization, but this is just one aspect of the larger study design issue. As agencies seek to report on habitat resources beyond the site-specific scale, sampling design considerations will become critical in the utility of data now being accumulated.

References

Aadland, L. P. 1993. Stream habitat types: their fish assemblages and relationship to flow. North American Journal of Fisheries Management 13:790–806.

Alexander, R. B., A. S. Ludtke, K. K. Fitzgerald, and T. L. Schertz. 1996. Data from selected U.S. Geological Survey National Stream Water-Quality Monitoring Networks (WQN) on CD-ROM. U.S. Geological Survey, Open-File Report 96-337, Reston, Virginia.

Allan, J. D. 1995. Stream ecology. Chapman and Hall, New York.

Angermeier, P. L., and I. J. Schlosser. 1995. Conserving aquatic biodiversity: beyond species and populations. Pages 402–414 *in* J. L. Nielsen, editor. Evolution and the aquatic ecosystem: defining unique units in population conservation. American Fisheries Society Symposium 17, Bethesda, Maryland.

APHA (American Public Health Association), American Water Works Association, and Water Pollution Control Federation. 1980. Standard methods for the examination of water and wastewater, 15th edition. APHA, Washington DC.

APHA (American Public Health Association), American Water Works Association, and Water Environment Federation. 1998. Standard methods for the examination of water and wastewater, 20th edition. APHA, Washington DC.

Armantrout, N. B. 1990. Aquatic habitat inventory. U.S. Bureau of Land Management, Eugene, Oregon.

Armantrout, N. B. 1996. Alaska Aquatic Resources Information Management System (AARIMS). U.S. Bureau of Land Management, Anchorage, Alaska.

Armantrout, N. B., compiler. 1998. Glossary of aquatic habitat inventory terminology. American Fisheries Society, Bethesda, Maryland.

Atwood, W. W. 1940. The physiographic provinces of North America. Ginn and Company, Boston, Massachusetts.

Auble, G. T., J. M. Friedman, and M. L. Scott. 1994. Relating riparian vegetation to present and future stream flows. Ecological Applications 4:544–554.

Bailey, R. G. 1978. Description of ecoregions of the United States. U.S. Forest Service, Intermountain Region, Ogden, Utah.

Bailey, R. G. 1983. Delineation of ecosystem regions. Environmental Management 7:365–373.

Bailey, R. G. 1995. Descriptions of ecoregions of the United States. U.S. Forest Service, Intermountain Region, Miscellaneous publication number 1391, Ogden, Utah.

Bailey, R. G. 1998. Ecoregions map of North America: explanatory note. U.S. Forest Service, Miscellaneous Publication 1548, Washington, DC.

Bailey, R. G., P. E. Avers, T. King, and W. H. McNab. 1994. Ecoregions and subregions of the United States (map). U.S. Geological Survey, Washington, DC.

Bailey, R. G., and H. C. Hogg. 1986. A world ecoregions map for resource reporting. Environmental Conservation 13:195–202.

Bailey, R. G., R. D. Pfister, and J. A. Henderson. 1978. Nature of land and resource classification—a review. Journal of Forestry 76:650–655.

Bain, M. B., J. T. Finn, and H. E. Booke. 1985. Quantifying stream substrate for habitat analysis studies. North American Journal of Fisheries Management 5:499–500.

Bain, M. B., T. C. Hughes, and K. K. Arend. 1999. Trends in methods for assessing freshwater habitats. Fisheries 24(4):16–21.

Baker, J. A., and S. A. Foster. 1992. Estimating density and abundance of endemic fishes in Hawaiian streams. Hawaii Department of Land and Natural Resources, Honolulu.

Baker, J. R., D. V. Peck, and D. W. Sutton. 1997. Environmental monitoring and assessment program, surface waters field operations manual for lakes. U.S. Environmental Protection Agency, EPA/600/R-97/003, Washington, DC.

Barnes, H. H., Jr. 1967. Roughness characteristics of natural channels. U.S. Geological Survey, Water-Supply Paper 1849, Reston, Virginia.

Baxter, R. M., and P. Glaude. 1980. Environmental effects of dams and impoundments. Canada Department of Fisheries and Oceans, Bulletin 205, Ottawa, Ontario.

Bell, M. 1986. Fisheries handbook of engineering requirements and biological criteria. U.S. Army Corps of Engineers, North Pacific Division, Fish Passage Development and Evaluation Program, Portland, Orgeon.

Bevenger, G. S., and R. M. King. 1995. A pebble count procedure for assessing watershed cumulative effects. U.S. Forest Service Research Paper RM-RP-319, Fort Collins, Colorado.

Binns, N. A. 1982. Habitat quality index procedures manual. Wyoming Game and Fish Department, Laramie, Wyoming.

Bisson, P. A., and D. R. Montgomery. 1996. Valley segments, stream reaches, and channel units. Pages 23–42 *in* R. F. Hauer and G. A. Lambert, editors. Methods in stream ecology. Academic Press, San Diego, California.

Bisson, P. A., J. L. Nielson, R. Palmason, and L. E. Grove. 1982. A system of naming habitat types in small streams, with examples of habitat utilization by salmonids during low stream flow. Pages 62–73 *in* N. B. Armantrout, editor. Acquisition and utilization of aquatic habitat inventory information. American Fisheries Society, Western Division, Bethesda, Maryland.

Bovee, K. D. 1982. A guide to stream habitat analysis using the in stream flow incremental methodology. U.S. Fish and Wildlife Service, FWS/OBS-82/26, Washington, DC.

Busch, W. D. N., and P. G. Sly. 1992. The development of an aquatic habitat classification system for lakes. CRC Press, Boca Raton, Florida.

Carpenter, J., and O. E. Maughan. 1993. Macrohabitat of Sonora chub (*Gila ditaenia*) in Sycamore Creek, Santa Cruz County, Arizona. Journal of Freshwater Ecology 8:265–280.

Chapman, D. W. 1988. Critical review of variables used to define fine sediment in redds of large salmonids. Transactions of the American Fisheries Society 117:1–21.

Chesser, W. L. 1975. Physiographic map of the earth. Brigham Young University, Provo, Utah.

Cline, L. D., R. A. Short, and J. V. Ward. 1982. The influence of highway construction on the macroinvertebrates and epilithic algae of a high mountain stream. Hydrobiologia 96:149–159.

Coghill, K. 1996. Stream survey protocol for the Tongass National Forest. U.S. Forest Service, Juneau, Alasaka.

Cole, G. A. 1975. Textbook of limnology. C. V. Mosby, St. Louis, Missouri.

Commission for Environmental Cooperation. 1997. Ecological regions of North America: toward a common perspective. Commission for Environmental Cooperation, Montreal, Quebec.

Cowardin, L. M., V. Carter, F. C. Golet, and E. T. LaRoe. 1979. Classification of wetlands and deepwater habitats of the United States. U.S. Fish and Wildlife Service, FWS-OBS-79/31, Washington, DC.

Crisp, D. T. 1990. Simplified methods of estimating daily mean stream water temperature. Freshwater Biology 23:457–462.

Cummins, K. W. 1962. An evaluation of some techniques for the collection and analysis of benthic samples with special emphasis on lotic waters. American Midland Naturalist 67:477–504.

Dana, P. H. 1998. Coordinate systems overview. University of Texas, Department of Geography, Austin.

Daubenmire, R. 1959. A canopy-coverage method of vegetational analysis. Northwest Science 33:43–64.

Dibble, E. D., K. J. Killgore, and S. L. Harrel. 1996. Assessment of fish-plant interactions. Pages 357–372 in L. E. Miranda and D. R. DeVries, editors. Multidimensional approaches to reservoir fisheries management. American Fisheries Society Symposium 16, Bethesda, Maryland.

Dodge, D. P., G. A. Goodchild, J. C. Tilt, and D. G. Waldriff. 1981. Manual of instructions: aquatic habitat inventory surveys. Ontario Ministry of Natural Resources, Fisheries Branch, Official Procedures Manual, Toronto.

Dolloff, C. A., D. G. Hankin, and G. H. Reeves. 1993. Basinwide estimation of habitat and fish populations in streams. U.S. Forest Service, Blacksburg, Virginia.

Duff, D., F. Mangum, and R. Maw. 1989. Fisheries habitat surveys handbook. U.S. Forest Service, Intermountain Region, Report FSH 2609.23, Ogden, Utah.

Dunne, T., and L. B. Leopold. 1978. Water in Environmental Planning. W. H. Freeman and Company, New York.

Dupuis, T., D. Guignion, R. MacFarlane, and R. Redmond. 1994. A technical manual for stream improvement on Prince Edward Island. Morell River Management Co-op, Charlottetown, Prince Edward Island, Canada.

Earhart, H. G. 1984. Monitoring total suspended solids by using nephelometry. Environmental Management 8:81–86.

Espegren, G. D. 1996. Development of instream flow recommendations in Colorado using R2CROSS. Colorado Water Conservation Board, Denver.

Everett, R. A., and G. M. Ruiz. 1993. Coarse woody debris as a refuge from predation in aquatic communities. Oecologia 93:475–486.

Fajen, O. F., and R. E. Wehnes. 1982. Missouri's method of evaluating stream habitat. Pages 117–123 in N. Armantrout, editor. Acquisition and utilization of aquatic habitat inventory information. American Fisheries Society, Western Division, Bethesda, Maryland.

Federal Interagency Committee on Water Resources. 1961. Notes on hydrologic activities, Bulletin 11: river basin maps showing hydrologic stations. U.S. Government Printing Office, Washington, DC.

Fenneman, N. M. 1931. Physiography of western United States. McGraw-Hill, New York.

Fenneman, N. M. 1938. Physiography of eastern United States. McGraw-Hill, New York.

Filipeck, S., D. J. Ebert, B. K. Wagner, J. A. Clingenpeel, W. M. Bivin, B. G. Cochran, and D. Patton. 1994. The basin area stream survey (BASS) system manual: a guide to evaluating the biological , physical and chemical aspects of streams and rivers. Arkansas Game and Fish Commision and U.S. Forest Service, Research Technical Report, Little Rock, Arkansas.

Fishman, M. J., J. W. Raese, C. N. Gerlitz, and R. A. Husband. 1994. U.S. Geological Survey approved inorganic and organic methods for the analysis of water and fluvial sediment, 1954–94: U.S. Geological Survey, Open-File Report 94-351, Reston, Virginia.

Flosi, G., and F. L. Reynolds. 1994. California salmonid stream habitat restoration manual. California Department of Fish and Game, Technical Report, Sacramento.

Frissell, C. A., W. J. Liss, C. E. Warren, and M. D. Hurley. 1986. A hierarchical framework for stream habitat classification: viewing streams in a watershed context. Environmental Management 10:199–214.

Galay, V. J., R. Kellerhals, and D. I. Bray. 1973. Diversity of river types in Canada. Pages 217–250 in Fluvial processes and sedimentation. Proceedings of hydrology symposium. National Research Council of Canada, Ottawa.

Gordon, N. E., T. A. McMahon, and B. L. Finlayson. 1992. Stream hydrology: an introduction for ecologists. John Wiley and Sons, New York.

Gregory, K. J., and D. E. Walling. 1973. Drainage basin form and process, a geomorphological approach. John Wiley and Sons, New York.

Growns, I. O., and J. A. Davis. 1994. Longitudinal changes in near-bed flows and macroinvertebrate communities in a western Australian stream. Journal of the North American Benthological Society 13:417–438.

Gubala, C. P., C. Branch, N. Roundy, and D. Landers. 1994. Automated global positioning system charting of environmental attributes: a limnologic case study. Science of the Total Environment 148:83–92.

Hach Company. 1992. Water analysis handbook. Hach Company, Loveland, Colorado.

Hadley, R. F. and S. A. Schumm. 1961. Sediment sources and drainage basin characteristics in upper Cheyenne River basin. U.S. Geological Survey, Water-Supply Paper 1531-B, Reston, Virginia.

Hagstrom, N. T., W. B. Gerrish, E. A. Machowski, and W. A. Hyatt. 1989. A survey of Connecticut streams and rivers—Farmington River, Park River, and Stony Brook drainages. Annual Performance Report FF-66-R-1, Connecticut Department of Environmental Protection, Hartford.

Hamilton, K., and E. P. Bergersen 1984. Methods to estimate aquatic habitat variables. Colorado State University, Cooperative Fish and Wildlife Research Unit, Fort Collins.

Hankin, D. G., and G. H. Reeves. 1988. Estimation total fish abundance and total habitat area in small streams based on visual estimation methods. Canadian Journal of Fisheries and Aquatic Sciences 45:834–844.

Hansen, P. L., R. D. Pfister, K. Boggs, B. J. Cook, J. Joy, and D. K. Hinckley. 1995. Classification and management of Montana's riparian and wetland sites. University of Montana, Montana Forest and Conservation Experiment Station, Miscellaneous Publication Number 54, Missoula.

Hanson, L. 1998. Physiographic provinces of the United States. Salem State College, Department of Geological Sciences, Salem, Massachusetts.

Harrelson, C. C., C. L. Rawlins, and J. P. Potyondy. 1994. Stream channel reference sites: an illustrated guide to field technique. U.S. Forest Service, Rocky Mountain Forest and Range Experiment Station, General Technical Report RM-245, Fort Collins, Colorado.

Hart, D. D. 1996. Fine-scale field measurements of benthic flow environmental inhabited by stream invertebrates. Limnology and Oceanography 41:297–308.

Harvey, C. A., and D. A. Eash. 1996. Description, instructions, and verification for Basinsoft, a computer program to quantify drainage-basin characteristics. U.S. Geological Survey, Water-Resources Investigations Report 95-4287, Reston, Virginia.

Hawkins, C. P., and 10 coauthors. 1993. A hierarchical approach to classifying stream habitat feature. Fisheries 18(6):3–12.

Hem, J. D. 1970. Study and interpretation of chemical characteristics of natural water. U.S. Geological Survey, Water-supply Paper 1473.

Horton, R. E. 1932. Drainage basin characteristics. Transactions of the American Geophysical Union 13:350–361.

Horton, R. E. 1945. Erosional development of streams and their drainage basins: hydrophysical approach to quantitative morphology. Bulletin of the Geological Society of America 56:275–350.

Hubert, W. A., and E. P. Bergersen. 1998. Define the purpose of habitat analysis and avoid the activity trap. Fisheries 23(5):20–21.

Hughes, R. M., D. P. Larsen, and J. M. Omernik. 1986. Regional reference sites: a method for assessing stream potentials. Environmental Management 10:629–635.

Hughes, R. M., E. Rexstad, and C. E. Bond. 1987. The relationship of aquatic ecoregions, river basins and physiographic provinces to the ichthyogeographic regions of Oregon. Copeia 2:423–432.

Hunt, C. B. 1967. Physiography of the United States. W. H. Freeman, San Francisco, California.

Hunter, C. J. 1991. Better trout habitat. Island Press, Washington, DC.

Hynes, H. B. N. 1975. The stream and its valley. Internationale Vereinigung für theoretische und angewandte Limnologie Verhandlungen 19:1–15.

Inter-agency Committee on Water Resources, Subcommittee on Hydrology. 1961. Notes on hydrologic activities, Bulletin 11 - river basin maps showing hydrologic stations. U.S. Government Printing Office, Washington, DC.

Jensen, M. E., I. Goodman, N. L. Poff, P. Bourgeron, J. R. Maxwell, C. J. Edwards, and D. Cleland. *In Press*. Use of ecological classification and mapping units in the characterization of aquatic systems for ecosystem management. Journal of the American Water Resources Association.

Johnson, J. H., Dropkin, D. S. and Shaffer, P. G. 1992. Habitat use by a headwater stream fish community in north central Pennsylvania. Rivers 3:69–79.

Jowett, I. G., J. Richardson, and R. M. McDowall. 1996. Relative effects of instream habitat and land use on fish distribution and abundance in tributaries of the Grey River, New Zealand. New Zealand Journal of Marine and Freshwater Research 30:463–475.

Kaufmann, P. R. and E. G. Robison. 1995. Physical habitat assessment. Section 6 *in* D. J. Klemm, and J. M. Lazorchak, editors. Environmental monitoring and assessment program. Surface waters: field operations and methods for measuring the ecological condition of wadeable streams. U.S. Environmental Protection Agency Report 620/R-94/004, Cincinnati, Ohio.

Kershner, J. L., H. L. Forsgren, and W. R. Meehan. 1991. Managing salmonid habitats. Pages 599–606 *in* W. R. Meehan, editor. Influences of forest and rangeland management on salmonid fishes and their habitats. American Fisheries Society, Special Publication 19, Bethesda, Maryland.

Kinsolving, A. D., and Bain, M. B. 1990. A new approach for measuring cover in fish habitat studies. Journal of Freshwater Ecology 5:373–378.

Kondolf, G. M., and S. Li. 1992. The pebble count technique for quantifying surface bed material size in instream flow studies. Rivers 3:80–87.

Koppen, W. 1931. Grundriss der klimakunde. Walter de Gruyter Company, Berlin, Germany.

Krueger, C. C., and D. J. Decker. 1993. The process of fisheries management. Pages 33–54 *in* C. C. Kohler and W. A. Hubert, editors. Inland fisheries management in North America. American Fisheries Society, Bethesda, Maryland.

Kunkle, H. S., and G. H. Comer. 1971. Estimating suspended sediment concentrations in streams by turbidity measurements. Journal of Soil and Water Conservation 26:18–20.

Lemly, A. D. 1982. Modification of benthic insect communities in polluted streams: combined effects of sedimentation and nutrient enrichment. Hydrobiologia 87:229–245.

Leopold, L. B., M. G. Wolman, and J. P. Miller. 1964. Fluvial processes in geomorphology. W. H. Freeman, San Francisco, California.

Lettenmaier, D. P., E. R. Hooper, C. Wagoner, and K. B. Faris. 1991. Trends in stream quality in the continental United States, 1978–1987. Water Resources Research 27:327–339.

Likens, G. E. and F. H. Bormann. 1974. Linkages between terrestrial and aquatic ecosystems. Bioscience 24:447–456.

Lind, O. T. 1974. Handbook of common methods in limnology. C. V. Mosby, Saint Louis, Missouri.

Lisle, T. E. 1986. Effects of woody debris on anadromous salmonid habitat, Prince of Wales Island, southeast Alaska. North American Journal of Fisheries Management 6:538–550.

Lobeck, A. K. 1948. Physiographic provinces of North America. Hammond Company, Maplewood, New Jersey.

Luckhurst, B. E., and K. Luckhurst. 1978. Analysis of the influence of substrate variables on coral reef fish communities. Marine Biology 49:317–323.

Lyons, J. 1989. Correspondence between the distribution of fish assemblages in Wisconsin streams and Omernik's ecoregions. American Midland Naturalist 122:163–182.

Maine State Planning Office. 1987. The Maine lakes study: a statewide inventory of Maine lakes. Maine State Planning Office, Augusta.

Maloney, T. J., A. S. Ludtke, and T. L. Krizman. 1994. Quality-assurance results for routine water analysis in U.S. Geological Survey laboratories, water year 1991. U.S. Geological Survey, Water-Resources Investigations Report 94-4046, Reston, Virginia.

Maryland State Archives. 1999. Maryland physiography. Maryland State Archives, Annapolis.

Maxwell, J. R., C. J. Edwards, M. E. Jensen, S. J. Paustian, H. Parrott, and D. M. Hill. 1995. A hierarchical framework of aquatic ecological units in North America (Nearctic Zone). U.S. Forest Service, North Central Forest Experiment Station, General Technical Report NC-176, St. Paul, Minnesota.

McMahon, T. E., A. V. Zale, and D. J. Orth. 1996. Aquatic habitat measurements. Pages 83–120 *in* B. R. Murphy and D. W. Willis, editors. Fisheries techniques, 2nd edition. American Fisheries Society, Bethesda, Maryland.

Meador, M. R., C. R. Hupp, T. F. Cuffney, and M. E. Gurtz. 1993. Methods for characterizing stream habitat as part of the National Water Quality Assessment Program. U.S. Geological Survey, Open File Rep. 93-408, Raleigh, North Carolina.

Meehan, W. R. 1991. Influences of forest and rangeland management on salmonid fishes and their habitats. American Fisheries Society Special Publication 19, American Fisheries Society, Bethesda, Maryland.

Miller, J. A. 1990. Alabama, Florida, Georgia, and South Carolina: ground water atlas of the United States. U.S. Geological Survey, Hydrologic Investigations Atlas HA-730-G, Reston, Virginia.

Miller, R. R. 1958. Origin and affinities of the freshwater fish fauna of western North America. Pages 187–222 *in* C. L. Hubbs, editor. Zoogeography. American Association for the Advancement Science, Washington, DC.

Minnesota Department of Natural Resources. 1993. Manual of instructions for lake survey. Minnesota Department of Natural Resources, Special Publication No. 147, St. Paul.

Mississippi Department of Wildlife Conservation. 1986. Guidelines for standardized lake and reservoir surveys. Mississippi Department of Wildlife Conservation, Jackson.

Missouri Department of Conservation. Undated. Stream habitat assessment device. Missouri Department of Conservation, Jefferson City.

Modde, T., R. C. Ford, and M. G. Parsons. 1991. Use of a habitat-based stream classification system for categorizing trout biomass. North American Journal of Fisheries Management 11:305–311.

Montgomery, D. R., and J. M. Buffington. 1983. Channel classification, prediction of channel response, and assessment of channel condition. University of Washington, Department of Geological Sciences and Quaternary Research Center, Report FW-SH10-93-002, Seattle.

Moore, K., K. Jones, and J. Dambacher. 1995. Methods for stream habitat surveys, version 5.1. Oregon Department of Fish and Wildlife, Corvallis.

Myers, L. H. 1989. Riparian area management: inventory and monitoring of riparian areas. U.S. Bureau of Land Management, Technical Report 1737-3, Washington, DC.

Naiman, R. J., D. G. Lonzarich, T. J. Beechie, and S. C. Ralph. 1992. General principles of classification and the assessment of conservation potential in rivers. *In* P. J. Boon, P. Calow, and G. E. Petts, editors. River Conservation and Management. John Wiley and Sons, London.

National Environmental Information Service. 1997. Index to U.S. EPA test methods. Baton Rouge, Louisiana.

National Wildlife Federation. 1995. Conservation directory. 40th edition. Washington, DC.

Natural Resources of Canada. 1999. Geodetic survey - software and related data products online demonstration. Natural Resources Canada, Geodetic Survey Division, Information Services Unit Geodetic Survey, Ottawa, Ontario.

New Brunswick Department of Natural Resources and Energy. Undated. Fishlake system. Department of Natural Resources, Fredericton, New Brunswick.

Newbury, R. W., and M. N. Gaboury. 1994. Stream analysis and fish habitat design, a field manual. Newbury Hydraulics Ltd., The Manitoba Habitat Heritage Corporation, Gibsons, British Columbia.

Olcott, P. G. 1995. Connecticut, Maine, Massachusetts, New Hampshire, New York, Rhode Island, and Vermont: Ground water atlas of the United States. U.S. Geological Survey, Hydrologic Investigations Atlas HA-730-M, Reston, Virginia.

Omernik, J. M. 1987. Aquatic ecoregions of the conterminous United States. Annals of the Association of American Geographers 77:118–125.

Omernik, J. M., and R. G. Bailey. 1997. Distinguishing between watersheds and ecoregions. Journal of the American Water Resources Association. 33: 935–949.

Omernik, J. M., and G. E. Griffith. 1991. Ecological regions verses hydrological units: frameworks for managing water quality. Journal of Soil and Water Conservation 46:334–340.

O'Neill, M. P., and A. D. Abrahams. 1987. Objective identification of pools and riffles. Water Resources Research 20:921–926.

Oregon Department of Fish and Wildlife. 1992. Quantitative reservoir habitat surveys 1992, aquatic inventory project. Oregon Department of Fish and Wildlife, Portland.

Orth, D. J. 1983. Aquatic habitat measurements. Pages 61–84 in L. A. Nielsen and D. L. Johnson, editors. Fisheries techniques. American Fisheries Society, Bethesda.

Petts, G. E. 1984. Impounded rivers. John Wiley & Sons, New York.

Pfankuch, D. J. 1975. Stream reach inventory and channel stability evaluation. U.S. Forest Service, Publication Ri-75-002, Missoula, Montana.

Pflieger, W. L. 1971. A distributional study of Missouri fishes. University of Kansas Publication, Museum of National History 20:225–570.

Pflieger, W. C. 1975. Fishes of Missouri. Missouri Department of Conservation, Jefferson City.

Plafkin, J. L., M. T. Barbour, K. D. Porter, S. K. Gross, and R. M. Hughes. 1989. Rapid bioassessment protocols for use in streams and rivers. U.S. Environmental Protection Agency, EPA/440/4-89-001, Washington, DC.

Platts, W. S., C. Armour, G. D. Booth, M. Bryant, J. L. Bufford, P. Cuplin, S. Jensen, G. W. Lienkaeemper, G. W. Minshall, S. B. Monsen, R. L. Nelson, J. R. Sedell, and J. S. Tuhy. 1987. Methods for evaluating riparian habitats with applications to management. U.S. Forest Service, General Technical Report INT-221, Ogden, Utah.

Platts, W. S., W. F. Megahan, and G. W. Minshall. 1983. Methods for evaluating stream, riparian, and biotic conditions. U.S. Forest Service, Intermountain Forest and Range Experiment Station, General Technical Report INT-138, Ogden, Utah.

Poole, G. C., C. A. Frissell, and S. C. Ralph. 1997. In-stream habitat unit classification: inadequacies for monitoring and some consequences for management. Water Resources Bulletin 33:879–896.

Potyondy, J. P., and T. Hardy. 1994. Use of pebble counts to evaluate fine sediment increase in stream channels. Water Resources Bulletin 30:509–520.

Powell, J. W. 1896. Physiographic regions of the United States. Pages 1–100 in National Geographic Society. The physiography of the United States; ten monographs. American Book Company, New York.

Pritt, J. W., and J. W. Raese. 1992. Quality assurance/quality control manual, National Water Quality Laboratory. U.S. Geological Survey, Open-File Report 92-495, Reston, Virginia.

Rankin, E. T. 1989. The qualitative habitat evaluation index [QHEI]: rationale, methods, and application. Ohio Environmental Protection Agency, Columbus.

Reiser, D. W. and R. T. Peacock. 1985. A technique for assessing upstream fish passage problems at small-scale hydropower developments. Pages 423–432 in F. W. Olson, R. G. White, and R. H. Hamre, editors. Symposium on small hydropower and fisheries. American Fisheries Society, Western Division, Bethesda, Maryland.

Rohm, C. M., J. W. Geise, and C. C. Bennett. 1987. Evaluation of an aquatic ecoregion classification of streams in Arkansas. Journal of Freshwater Ecology 4:127–140.

Roper, B. B., and D. L. Scarnecchia. 1995. Observer variability in classifying habitat types in stream surveys. North American Journal of Fisheries Management 15:49–53.

Rosgen, D. L. 1994. A classification of natural rivers. Catena 22:169–199.

Rosgen, D. L. 1996. Applied river morphology. Wildland Hydrology, Pagosa Springs, Colorado.

Seaber, P. R., F. P. Kapinos, and G. L. Knapp. 1994. Hydrologic unit maps. U.S. Geological Survey, Water-Supply Paper 2294, Denver, Colorado.

Scruton, D. A., T. C. Anderson, C. E. Bourgeois, and J. P. O'Brien. 1992. Small stream surveys for public-sponsored habitat improvement and enhancement projects. Canadian Report of Fisheries and Aquatic Sciences No. 2163.

Shreve, R. L. 1967. Infinite topologically random channel networks. Journal of Geology 75:178–186.

Simonson, T. D., J. Lyons, and P. D. Kanehl. 1993. Guidelines for evaluating fish habitat in Wisconsin streams. U.S. Forest Service, North Central Forest Experiment Station, General Technical Report NC-164, St. Paul, Minnesota.

Simonson, T. D., J. Lyons, and P. D. Kanehl. 1994. Quantifying fish habitat in streams: transect spacing, sample size, and a proposed framework. North American Journal of Fisheries Management 14:607–615.

Smith, R. A., R. B. Alexander, and K. J. Lanfear. 1993. Stream water quality in the conterminous United States — status and trends of selected indicators during the 1980's. U.S. Geological Survey, Water Supply Paper 2400, Reston, Virginia.

Smith, R. A., R. B. Alexander, and M. G. Wolman. 1987. Water-quality trends in the nation's rivers. Science 235:1607–1615.

Stalnaker, C., B. L. Lamb, J. Henriksen, K. Bovee, and J. Bartholow. 1995. The instream flow incremental methodology: a primer for IFIM. U.S. National Biological Service, Biological Report 29, Washington, DC.

Sternberg, R. B. 1978. Minnesota stream survey manual. Minnesota Department of Natural Resources, Special Publication 120, St. Paul.

Strahler, A. N. 1964. Quantitative geomorphology of drainage basins and channel networks. Pages 39–76 in V. T. Chow, editor. Handbook of applied hydrology, McGraw-Hill, New York.

Swanson, S., R. Miles, S. Leonard, and K. Genz. 1988. Classifying rangeland riparian areas; the Nevada task force approach. Journal of Soil and Water Conservation 43:259–263.

Tabor, R. A., and W. A. Wurtsbaugh. 1991. Predation risk and the importance of cover for juvenile rainbow trout in lentic systems. Transactions of the American Fisheries Society 120:728–738.

Tebo, L. B. 1955. Effects of siltation, resulting from improper logging, on the bottom fauna of a small trout stream in the southern Appalachians. The Progressive Fish-Culturist 17:64–70.

Texas Bureau of Economic Geology. 1998. The physiography of Texas. Texas Geological Survey, University of Texas, Austin.

Trautman, M. B. 1981. The fishes of Ohio. Ohio State University Press, Columbus.

Trewartha, G. T. 1968. An introduction to weather and climate. McGraw-Hill, New York.

University of Montana. 1999. Idaho hydrologic unit codes. University of Montana, School of Forestry, Riparian and Wetland Research Program, Missoula, Montana.

U.S. Department of Agriculture. 1963. Atlas of river basins of the United States. Soil Conservation Service, Washington, DC.

U.S. Department of Agriculture. 1970. Atlas of river basins of the United States. Soil Conservation Service, Washington, DC.

U.S. Environmental Protection Agency. 1976. Quality criteria for water. U.S. Environmental Protection Agency, Washington, DC.

U.S. Environmental Protection Agency. 1982. Handbook for sampling and sample preservation of water and wastewater. U.S. Environmental Protection Agency, EPA-600/4-82-029, Washington, DC.

U.S. Environmental Protection Agency. 1983. Methods for chemical analysis of water and wastes. U.S. Environmental Protection Agency, Washington, DC.

U.S. Environmental Protection Agency. 1986. Quality criteria for water 1986. U.S. Environmental Protection Agency, Office of Water Regulations and Standards, EPA 440/5-86-001, Washington, DC.

U.S. Environmental Protection Agency. 1994. USEPA Reach File Version 3.0, Alpha release (RF3-Alpha) technical reference. U.S. Environmental Protection Agency, Office of Wetlands, Oceans and Watersheds, Washington, DC.

U.S. Environmental Protection Agency. 1996. Level III ecoregions of the continental United States. U.S. Environmental Protection Agency, Office of Information Resources Management, Washington, D.C.

U.S. Environmental Protection Agency. 1997. The quality of our Nation's water: 1994. U.S. Environmental Protection Agency, Office of Wetlands, Oceans, and Watersheds, Washington, DC.

U.S. Fish and Wildlife Service. 1980. Habitat evaluation procedures (HEP). U.S. Fish and Wildlife Service, Ecological Services Manual 102, Washington, DC.

U.S. Geological Survey. 1973. Catalog of information on water data, 1972 edition. U.S. Geological Survey, Office of Water Data Coordination, Reston, Virginia.

U.S. Geological Survey. 1982. Chemical and physical quality of water and sediment. Chapter 5 in National handbook of recommended methods for water-data acquistion. U.S. Geological Survey, Office of Water Data Coordination, Reston, Virginia.

U.S. Geological Survey. 1997. Omernik ecoregions data. U.S. Geological Survey, EROS Data Center, Sioux Falls, South Dakota.

U.S. Geological Survey. 1998. Physiographic divisions. U.S. Geological Survey, Water Resources Division, Portland, Oregon.

U.S. Geological Survey. 1999a. Geographic names information system. U.S. Geological Survey, Reston, Virginia.

U.S. Geological Survey. 1999b. Physical divisions of the central region. U.S. Geological Survey, Biological Resources Division, Central Regional Office, Denver, Colorado.

U.S. National Bureau of Standards. 1983. Codes for the identification of hydrologic units in the Unites States and the Caribbean outlying areas. U.S. Department of Commerce, Federal Information Processing Standards Publication 103, Washington, DC.

U.S. Water Resources Council. 1970. Water resources regions and subregions for the national assessment of water and related land resources. U.S. Department of the Interior, Washington, DC.

Wahl, K. L., W. O. Thomas, Jr., and R. M. Hirsch. 1995. Stream-gaging program of the U.S. Geological Survey. U.S. Geological Survey, Circular 1123, Reston, Virginia.

Ward, J. V., and J. A. Stanford. 1979. The ecology of regulated streams. Plenum. New York.

Warren, C. E. 1979. Toward classification and rationale for watershed management and stream protection. U.S. Environmental Protection Agency, EPA/600/3-79/059, Corvallis, Oregon.

Waters, T. F. 1995. Sediment in Streams. American Fisheries Society, Monograph 7, Bethesda, Maryland.

Wentworth, C. K. 1922. A scale of grade and class for elastic sediments. Journal of Geology 30:377–392.

Wetzel, R. G., and G. E. Likens. 1990. Limnological analyses. Springer-Verlag, New York.

Whittier, T. R., R. M. Hughes, and D. P. Larsen. 1988. Correspondence between ecoregions and spatial patterns in stream ecosystems in Oregon. Canadian Journal of Fisheries and Aquatic Sciences 45:1264–1278.

Wiken, E. 1986. Terrestrial ecozones of Canada. Environment Canada, Ecological Land Classification Series Number 19, Hull, Quebec.

Williams, G. P. and M. G. Wolman. 1984. Downstream effects of dams on alluvial rivers. U.S. Geological Survey, Professional Paper 1286, Reston, Virginia.

Willis, D. W., and B. R. Murphy. 1996. Planning for sampling. Pages 1–15 *in* B. R. Murphy and D. W. Willis, editors. Fisheries techniques, 2nd edition. American Fisheries Society, Bethesda, Maryland.

Winger, P. V. 1981. Physical and chemical characteristics of warmwater streams: a review. Pages 32–44 *in* L. A. Krumholz, editor. The warmwater streams symposium, American Fisheries Society, Southern Division, Bethesda, Maryland.

Wolman, M. G. 1954. A method of sampling coarse river-bed material. Transactions of the American Geophysical Union 35:951–956.

Vermont Fish and Wildlife Department. 1988. Winhall River tributaries Atlantic salmon habitat survey, Appendix I: stream survey methodology. Vermont Fish and Wildlife Department, Job Performance Report, Project No. F-12-R-21, Montpelier.

Index